SIBO SUMMER COOKBOOK

60 recipes for people treating Small Intestinal Bacterial Overgrowth

Rebecca Coomes • The Healthy Gut

SIBO Summer Cookbook
1st US Edition 2017

First published in Australia in 2016 by
The Healthy Gut
PO Box 1405
East Camberwell LPO VIC 3126
Australia

Recipes: Rebecca Coomes
Editors: Rebecca Coomes, Aramenta Sobchak, and Kate Saunders-Morgan
Creative Director: Rebecca Coomes
Photography: Rebecca Coomes
Design and typesetting: Yedah Merino Designs
Prop and food styling: Rebecca Coomes
Food preparation: Rebecca Coomes

ISBN: 978-0-9944520-6-1

thehealthygut.co

contents

SIBO Recipes By Phase 4
Acknowledgments 6
Welcome 7
Foreword 8
My Story 10
What is SIBO? 12
SIBO Treatment Options 16
The SIBO Bi-Phasic Diet Protocol 20
SIBO Recipes
- Breakfasts 29
- Lunches 47
- Dinners 65
- Sides and Appetizers 83
- Desserts 95
- Snacks 113
- Dressings, Condiments and Fats 129
- Drinks 135

Glossary 144
Resources 147
Live Well With SIBO 152
Index 153

SIBO recipes by phase

phase 1 diet: reduce and repair

♥ Restricted

Breakfasts

Asian breakfast bowl . . . 35
Hot smoked salmon breakfast bowl . . . 33
Lemony scrambled eggs with smoked trout . . . 37
Prosciutto, egg, and red pepper muffins . . . 31
Zucchini fritters with crispy bacon and smoky salsa . . . 39

Lunches

Aussie-style burger with the works and a side of carrot fries . . . 59
Crispy salt and pepper calamari salad with lime aioli . . . 61
Marinated lamb skewers with a Greek salad . . . 49
San choy bao . . . 57
Zesty fish cakes with dipping sauce . . . 55

Dinners

Best ever steak with an arugula, tomato, and prosciutto salad . . . 69
Crispy chicken strips with lime aioli . . . 75
Lemon and lime BBQ snapper . . . 71
Marinated shrimp . . . 77
SIBO-ghetti and meatballs . . . 79
SIBO pizza with the works . . . 67
Thai-style marinated chicken drumsticks . . . 81

Sides and Accompaniments

Coleslaw . . . 89
Crunchy Asian salad . . . 93
French-style salad . . . 87
Greek-style salad . . . 91
Italian-style pan-fried broccoli . . . 85

Desserts

Mojito popsicles . . . 101

Snacks

Chunky roast pumpkin and macadamia dip with fresh vegetables . . . 115
Salt and pepper pork rinds . . . 125
Salt and vinegar smashed sardines . . . 121
Smoked paprika kale chips . . . 123
Spiced trail mix . . . 119

Dressings, condiments, and fats

Asian dressing . . . 132
Beef tallow . . . 133
French dressing . . . 132
Ghee . . . 132
Italian dressing . . . 132
Lemon aioli . . . 131
Lime aioli . . . 131
Mayonnaise . . . 131
Pork lard . . . 133
Smoky salsa . . . 130

Drinks

Chilled turmeric tea . . . 137
Virgin mojito . . . 141

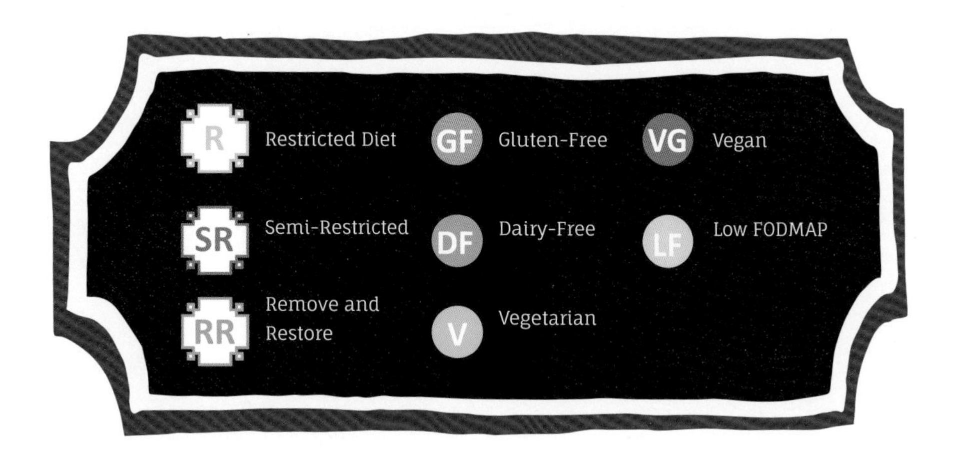

♥ Semi-Restricted

Breakfasts

Berry good breakfast bowl . . . 45
Breakfast smoothies . . . 41
Vanilla and cinnamon granola . . . 43

Lunches

Crunchy chicken tacos with coleslaw and guacamole . . . 63
Salmon tartare . . . 51

Dinners

Succulent lamb chops with a pomegranate, pecan, and pumpkin salad . . . 73

Desserts

Raspberry soufflé . . . 109
Summer pineapple with coconut whip . . . 105
Vanilla and strawberry coconut ice . . . 97

Snacks

Chai-spiced banana muffins . . . 117
Smoked trout dip . . . 127

Drinks

Iced coffee . . . 139
Summer punch . . . 143

phase 2 diet: remove and restore

Breakfasts

Chocolate granola . . . 43

Lunches

Crustless quiche Lorraine . . . 53

Desserts

Choc chip mini pancakes with berry coulis and coconut cream . . . 103
Choco-coco-nutty bites . . . 111
Chocolate bark . . . 99
Decadent mocha mousse . . . 107

Drinks

Iced hot chocolate . . . 139

acknowledgments

A cookbook doesn't come together on its own. There have been many people who have been instrumental in supporting me to launch this book.

Firstly, I would like to thank all of the recipe testers who graciously offered their precious time to read and test my recipes at home. Your input has been wonderful. A big shout-out also goes to my friends who let me borrow various items that featured in this cookbook.

I would also like to personally thank Cressida, a fellow woman with SIBO. It was fate that brought us into each other's lives and she has been an invaluable support and sounding board as I developed this cookbook.

Dr. Nirala Jacobi has kindly allowed me to use her SIBO Bi-Phasic Diet Protocol in this book, for which I am extremely grateful. Thank you for providing me further insight and information on SIBO and graciously sparing your very busy schedule for me.

The food wouldn't look as good as it does without the expert guidance and tuition from Aliki and Michael Dimitrakopoulos at Soul Impressions Photography. They are seriously amazing food photographers and gave me their time, coaching, and guidance to make my food the hero of the page.

To my friends, family, and partners of The Healthy Gut, thank you for supporting, encouraging, and guiding me over the course of this journey. I am lucky to have you in my life.

And finally, I can't thank my parents enough for their support. They have been recipe testers, food critics, photography stylists, set builders, sous chefs, dish hands, and everything in between. They allowed me to invade their home and fill it with food and equipment while I prepared and photographed this cookbook. Their love, encouragement, and support is always unwavering and this would have been a much more difficult journey without it. I love you mum and dad.

welcome

Welcome to the SIBO Summer Cookbook and thank you so much for purchasing it. The simple fact that you have bought a copy means more to me than you can possibly imagine. This comes to you with a lot of love and I hope you find it useful through your journey treating your SIBO.

As I healed myself of SIBO, I decided that I didn't want this condition to stop me from feeling joy, love, and passion for great food. Despite being given a restricted protocol to follow, it is still possible to relish great-tasting food. I look forward to taking you on a journey of the taste buds.

Rebecca x

foreword

Rebecca's beautiful cookbooks are filled with delicious recipes based on a version of the SIBO Specific Food Guide: The SIBO Bi-Phasic Diet. I created the SIBO Specific Food Guide to bring together two different SIBO diets, the Specific Carbohydrate Diet and the Low FODMAP Diet, along with my clinical experience.

Each of these diets significantly helped symptoms in my patients, but when combined into the SIBO Specific Food Guide, the success was even greater. The results are a dramatic improvement in both gastrointestinal and overall health.

My hope was that practitioners would customize the SIBO Specific Food Guide into more specific diet plans for their patients. That's just what Dr. Nirala Jacobi did with the SIBO Bi-Phasic Diet, and countless doctors and patients have benefited from it.

One can feel the warmth and healing emanating from the pages. Cookbooks are one of the best resources for SIBO patients, offering a valuable tool during treatment. With the American versions of her popular cookbooks, more taste buds can be delighted while health is restored. Thank you Rebecca for these beautiful, healthy, helpful books.

Dr. Allison Siebecker, ND, MSOM, LAc

siboinfo.com

In my years of treating SIBO, the most difficult commitment for my patients has been the SIBO diet. It is an intentionally restrictive diet to reduce the fermentation of food by bacteria in the small intestines. In addition to treatment, I designed this two-phased diet for people to follow for three months, but because it makes them feel so much better, people typically stay on it longer. Once treatment is completed, however, transitioning to a whole foods, varied diet is the goal.

There are many resources for SIBO diets on the Internet, but in my experience, most are far too lenient (or confusing) and that can lead to SIBO relapses.

I am so glad that Rebecca has written this book, and especially glad since she herself has overcome SIBO with the right treatment and diet protocol (as I recommend on www.sibotest.com). What better person to write this book than someone who has experienced it herself.

The phased diet tables are easy to understand and the recipes are delicious. I am thankful that SIBO sufferers will now have this valuable tool to help them navigate through the treatment towards the path of health.

Dr. Nirala Jacobi, BHSc, ND

sibotest.com

my story

In early 2015, I was diagnosed with SIBO. I felt such immense relief when I was given that diagnosis. I finally had an answer to the myriad of problems I had been suffering from for most of my life. I could have kissed my Naturopath for not only believing in me when I said I felt sick, but also knowing where to look to uncover the underlying problem.

Relief was quickly overtaken by anxiety. What was I going to eat now? I was already on a restricted diet, having cut out gluten and most dairy years ago. I had become ever intolerant to foods with the passing years so, already, I felt like I was operating out of a narrow food spectrum.

Initially, I felt overwhelmed and didn't know where to start. I went looking for SIBO-friendly recipes, but found that many were much more relaxed and used ingredients that were banned on Dr. Nirala Jacobi's SIBO Bi-Phasic Diet Protocol.

When I commenced my journey, I decided that I wanted to rid myself of SIBO as quickly as possible. I made a pact with myself that I would be 100% compliant 100% of the time. I didn't want to give the SIBO an opportunity to grow again and I wanted to move forward with my health once and for all. Apart from one small slip up three months into my treatment, I remained true to my word and was declared SIBO-free six months later.

Since commencing my journey, I have spoken to countless people who feel just as lost and confused as I once did over their health concerns. Other people with SIBO have told me of their fear of food and confusion over what to eat.

I am a foodie at heart and suspect I was a chef in another life. My first memory of cooking is from when I was three years old, standing in my grandmother's kitchen, baking a sponge cake. I was blessed to have some excellent cooks in my family, and they shared their love of cooking and knowledge of food with me. I have taught many friends how to cook over the years, and love nothing more than throwing open my doors, cooking up a feast, and celebrating life with my friends over good food and excellent conversation.

The kitchen is a place where I find solace. After a tough day, I am always at my most relaxed and happiest creating a dish from scratch. After my initial frustration, I used my SIBO treatment as an exciting challenge. I was inspired to create food that would interest me and this cookbook is a reflection of the many recipes I created during that time.

I believe in eating food when it is in season and that is why this cookbook has a focus on summer produce, and should be used ideally in the warmer months. It is at its freshest and has traveled the fewest miles. I always choose free-range meat, eggs, and poultry and I want the animal to have lived a life as close to normal, being free to roam without the heavy use of antibiotics or grain feed. There are some amazing producers who are growing and raising incredible produce. Get to know your local butcher, fishmonger, and grocer. They will help point you in the right direction.

I am passionate about showing others that SIBO doesn't have to signal an end to good food. Yes, we have to be more restricted for a period of time, but we are left with such healthy, nutritious, whole foods options. All we need is a little bit of creativity and we would never know it is a SIBO meal.

what is SIBO?

what is SIBO?

Small Intestinal Bacterial Overgrowth (SIBO) is a chronic bacterial overgrowth in the small intestine. This bacteria normally live in the gastrointestinal tract, but have overgrown in an area they're not supposed to be in such large numbers, causing havoc. It is estimated that on average 60% of people with Irritable Bowel Syndrome (IBS) are experiencing their symptoms due to SIBO. If you experience the following symptoms, you may have SIBO:

* Bloating
* Cramping
* Constipation
* Diarrhea
* Alternating constipation and diarrhea
* Food sensitivities
* Belching and flatulence
* Nausea
* Heartburn
* Fatigue
* Chronic digestive complaints
* Abdominal cramping and pain
* Joint pain
* Skin symptoms (e.g., eczema, rashes)
* Iron and B12 deficiency
* Respiratory symptoms (e.g., asthma)
* Mood symptoms (i.e., depression, anxiety)
* Brain symptoms (i.e., autism)

what causes SIBO?

It is believed that SIBO can be caused by a structural or functional abnormality of the small intestine. The risk factors for this occurring are many, including:

* Food poisoning
* Gastroenteritis
* Gastrointestinal infection
* Antibiotic use
* Acid blockers
* Fungus overgrowth
* Surgical intervention and operations to the abdomen (e.g., Appendectomy, C-section, etc.)
* Endometriosis
* A dysfunctional ileocecal valve
* Hypothyroidism
* Stress
* Diabetes
* Initial poor colonization of gut bacteria due to caesarian birth and/or lack of breastfeeding

what does SIBO do to you?

Instead of allowing the villi and microvilli in your small intestine to absorb nutrients from the food, the bacteria digest it instead, causing it to ferment. A bi-product of the bacteria's digestion is methane and/or hydrogen gas, which is only produced by the bacteria and not our bodies.

These gases cause bloating, flatulence, cramping, diarrhea, belching, constipation, and more. It is also believed this gas can cause leaky gut syndrome, where the wall of the gut becomes permeable and allows food particles through to the blood stream, which creates an immune response.

The other side effect of SIBO is damage to the villi and microvilli, which results in nutrients not being absorbed. When the bacteria digest your food, it means they're taking a lot of the nutrients before they make it to you, which leads to malabsorption of monosaccharides, amino acids, vitamins (especially B12 and folic acid), and minerals (especially magnesium, iron, and calcium).

Some side effects of poor nutrient absorption can include fatigue, hormonal imbalances, and restless leg syndrome.

Other damage caused by the bacterial overgrowth can be the suspension of the natural muscular wave, the migrating motor complex that occurs every ninety minutes, to push food along. This further increases the time food spends in the small intestine and its ability to ferment.

Foods containing fermentable fiber, starch, lactose, and fructose can make SIBO symptoms worse. Foods like gluten, grains, starches like potatoes, legumes, fruits, and some vegetables can be problematic. And despite the promotion that we should be having a high-fiber diet with the use of fiber supplements, this can exacerbate the problem and people with SIBO can feel worse, not better, when using supplements.

SIBO generates toxins, which put pressure on the lymphatic system, the immune system, and our body's own detoxification system.

Unfortunately, SIBO goes largely undiagnosed, which can result in years of damage to the small intestine. People may develop intolerances to certain foods like gluten, lactose, or fructose as the small intestine becomes less equipped to manage it.

It can be difficult to treat other digestive problems if SIBO remains present, and the longer it remains in the small intestine, the more damage it can cause.

conditions associated with SIBO

There are a number of conditions that are known to be associated with SIBO. These include:

* Irritable Bowel Syndrome (IBS)
* Acid reflux
* Celiac disease
* Chronic Fatigue Syndrome
* Fibromyalgia
* Chronic constipation
* Inflammatory Bowel Disease (e.g., Crohn's and ulcerative colitis)
* Diabetes
* Restless leg syndrome
* Acne rosacea
* Hyperthyroidism
* Scleroderma
* Chronic Prostatitis
* Non-alcoholic Steatohepatitis (NASH)
* Liver cirrhosis
* Diverticulitis

Sources: siboinfo.com and sibotest.com

SIBO treatment options

SIBO treatment options

Currently, SIBO can be treated through three options: antibiotics, herbal antibiotics, and the Elemental Diet.

♥ antibiotics

Antibiotics are often a preferred treatment option for gastroenterologists and patients alike, as they seek to attack the bacterial overgrowth quickly. Rifaximin and Neomycin are the most commonly prescribed antibiotics for SIBO, as they are almost completely non-absorbable and stay within the small intestine. This means they have a localized action and don't cause systemic or widespread side effects.

♥ herbal antibiotics

Herbal antibiotics also seek to attack the excess bacteria directly by reducing the number of bacteria living in the small intestine. Herbs are often the first choice for alternative practitioners, naturopaths, and integrative physicians. They do take longer to take effect, so for every week on an antibiotic, two weeks are required on an herbal antibiotic.

Studies have shown that herbal therapies are as effective as Rifaximin and have a similar response rate and safety profile. Some of the most commonly used herbs include allicin, oregano, berberine, and neem, among others. Like all treatments, the correct herbal protocol needs to be determined for each individual patient and their specific type of SIBO.

♥ the elemental diet

The Elemental Diet replaces meals with a liquid pre-digested diet, which seeks to starve the bacteria while providing the individual with amino acids, carbohydrates, fats, vitamins, and minerals, which are absorbed in the upper digestive tract.

The Elemental Diet can be made at home or purchased in over-the-counter formulations. Some formulations taste better than others and this diet can be challenging, as it requires a complete liquid diet for at least two weeks. Some patients also complain of dramatic weight loss, which can be problematic for those already underweight.

The Elemental Diet is believed to have a high success rate in the treatment of SIBO, but it has many challenges, including cost, taste, food deprivation, and weight loss. It is often a last resort for patients.

Some patients only need to do one of the three treatment options to recover from SIBO. However, for two thirds of people, SIBO is a chronic, recurring condition and multiple rounds are required of one or all three of the available treatments.

♥ nutrition

In addition to the treatment protocol, a patient's nutrition is important in supporting the recovery from SIBO. It is believed that diet alone cannot cure SIBO and instead is used to support treatment and provide relief from digestive symptoms.

A restricted diet is designed to be used only for a short time. It is important to reintroduce a wide range of foods and fermentable fibers, as they feed the broader gut microbiome.

In addition, it needs to be understood why the body developed SIBO in the first place. Just as bloating can be a symptom of SIBO, SIBO is a symptom of an underlying condition that has allowed the bacteria to migrate and multiply in the small intestine. Understanding and addressing the underlying cause should occur to achieve a permanent recovery from SIBO.

Source: siboinfo.com

the 5 key pillars of health

Along with the treatment protocols currently available for SIBO, the five key pillars of health should be addressed to achieve lasting health and happiness.

AWARENESS

NUTRITION

MOVEMENT

MINDSET

LIFESTYLE

The first step to regaining your health is to become aware of how you are feeling. Understanding your symptoms and what they mean is an important first step in your recovery.

AWARENESS

Nutrition is vital to living a healthy gut life. With SIBO, the food you eat can help or hinder your progress. Awareness of what you eat and how you eat is essential to your recovery.

NUTRITION

Our bodies are designed to move. Our gut can respond positively to exercise and movement. Learn how you move your body beneficially and what type of movement will help or hinder your recovery.

MOVEMENT

A positive mindset has an impact on our health. When you have been unwell, it can be very easy to fall into a negative mindset. Turning negative thoughts into positive beliefs will support you to achieve wellness.

MINDSET

The way you live your life is fundamental to your recovery. Stress, sleep, relationships, social activities, relaxation, and goal setting play an important role in how quickly you regain your health.

LIFESTYLE

the SIBO bi-phasic diet protocol

the SIBO bi-phasic diet protocol

This cookbook has been developed in compliance with Dr. Nirala Jacobi's SIBO Bi-Phasic Diet Protocol and has a range of recipes that are suitable for every phase of the diet. Each recipe has been classified depending on the phase it adheres to, while also listing other dietary classifications, such as gluten-free, dairy-free, low FODMAP, vegetarian, or vegan.

This cookbook has been developed as a tool to support your journey through the active treatment phase. However, it is advisable to speak with your Practitioner and modify the diet as necessary to accommodate any food intolerances or allergies.

what is the SIBO bi-phasic diet?

The SIBO Bi-Phasic Diet has been based on the low FODMAP Diet and the Specific Carbohydrate Diet, to support the elimination of the bacterial overgrowth in the small intestine.

PHASE 1: REDUCE AND REPAIR (4-6 WEEKS)

The first phase of the diet eliminates all grains, legumes, dairy, sugar, certain vegetables, canned foods, processed foods, fermented foods, and alcohol. The removal of these foods prioritizes the repair of disturbed digestion.

REDUCE The first phase of the diet focuses on reducing fermentable starches and fibers. This is necessary to starve the bacteria of their preferred fuel so that they die off and reduce their numbers in the small intestine.

REPAIR It is important to repair the damage to the intestinal lining as well as repair proper digestion.

Phase 1 is divided into two groups:

♥ Phase 1 Restricted Diet R

Commence in the Restricted Diet phase, and move to the Semi-Restricted Diet phase once your symptoms decrease. The duration depends on how quickly your symptoms improve. If your symptoms are greatly improved after the first week, talk to your Practitioner about moving into the Semi-Restricted Diet. If at any point during treatment you suffer a relapse of symptoms, return to the Restricted Diet until your symptoms subside.

♥ Phase 1 Semi-Restricted Diet SR

This diet builds on the Restricted Diet by increasing some quantities of foods, adding in some fruits, sugars, limited alcohol, and some starches such as rice and quinoa. Your Practitioner may start you on this level if you are prone to rapid weight loss or need more energy from starches.

PHASE 2: REMOVE AND RESTORE (6 WEEKS +)

This phase builds on the allowable foods from Phase 1 and also sees the introduction of some dairy and increased quantities of certain foods. Be aware of any symptoms that arise and work closely with your Practitioner before moving to this phase and adding new foods into your diet.

REMOVE Remaining overgrown bacteria and fungi are removed from the small intestine through the use of antimicrobials as prescribed by your Practitioner. Even though still a low-fiber diet, the protocol becomes more lenient to allow for some bacterial growth so that antimicrobials are more successful.

RESTORE The restoration of the normal motility of the small intestine is important to prevent a SIBO relapse. In this phase, your Practitioner may prescribe prokinetic medication or supplements.

common food reactions

Chronic SIBO patients can be prone to food reactions. Seemingly healthy food can cause reactions such as itching, hives, joint pain, and a host of other symptoms. The most common culprits are Histamine, Oxalates, and Salicylates. These substances normally tolerated in food can cause problems when the digestive tract is inflamed and reactive. Healing the small intestine can lead to resolution of these reactions.

histamine

Histamine is a biogenic amine which is naturally high in certain foods. Symptoms include headaches, bloating, cramping, insomnia, itching, and allergies. Histamine is particularly high in: aged meats, bone broth (which has been cooked for hours), spinach, and tinned fish or meats.

oxalates

Oxalates are natural molecules abundant in green leafy vegetables and certain other plant based foods. They can also cause gut reactions by irritating the mucosal lining. Symptoms include: joint pain, kidney stones, and vulvar pain. High oxalate foods include: almonds, beet greens, cocoa, quinoa, rhubarb, silver beet, and spinach.

salicylates

Salicylates are natural plant substances which help the plant defend itself against bacteria, fungi and other pests. They are toxic to everyone in very high doses, but the threshold is much lower with a salicylate sensitivity. Symptoms include: headaches, itching, puffy or burning eyes, nausea, sinus congestion, and stomach pain. High salicylates foods include: avocado, berries, coconut oil, nightshade vegetables (bell pepper, chili pepper, eggplant, and tomato), olive oil, radish, and zucchini.

Source: sibotest.com

the SIBO bi-phasic diet

	PHASE 1 DIET >> REDUCE AND REPAIR		
	RESTRICTED DIET	SEMI-RESTRICTED Add (or increase) these foods to the Restricted Diet	AVOID Until further notice
PROTEIN	Eggs, fish, meat, poultry	Eggs, fish, meat, poultry	All legumes
DAIRY PRODUCTS	Avoid	Avoid	Avoid
VEGETABLES Unlimited	Alfalfa sprouts, arugula, bamboo shoots, bell peppers, bok choy, carrot, chives, cucumber, eggplant, endive, ginger, kale, lettuce, olives, radicchio, radish, scallion (green part only), sunflower sprouts, tomatoes/sun-dried	Parsnip, scallion	Potato: sweet, white Starch powder: arrowroot, corn, rice, tapioca Canned vegetables, garlic, mushrooms, onions
VEGETABLES Limited to 1 of the following per meal	Asparagus – 1 spear Artichoke hearts – 1/8 cup Beet – 2 slices Broccoli – ½ cup Brussels sprouts – 2 ea Cabbage: green/red – ½ cup Cabbage: Napa/Savoy – ¾ cup Cauliflower – ½ cup Celery – 1 stick Celery root – ½ cup Chili pepper – 4 inches/1 oz Fennel bulb – ½ cup Green beans –10 ea Peas: green – 1/4 cup Snow peas – 5 pods Spinach –15 leaves Squash/Pumpkin – 1/4 cup Zucchini – ¾ cup	Asparagus – 2-3 spears Brussels sprouts – ½ cup Leek – ½ ea Spinach > 15 leaves/5 oz Squash/Pumpkin – ½ cup Zucchini – 1 cup	
FRUIT Limited to 2 servings per day	Lemon Lime	Avocado - ¼ Banana - ½ Berries: all varieties - ½ cup Cantaloupe - ¼ cup Cherries - 3 Citrus - 1 piece Grapes - 10 Honeydew - ¼ cup Kiwi - 1 piece Lychee - 5 Papaya - ¼ cup Passion fruit - 1 piece Pineapple - ¼ cup Pomegranate - ½ small or ¼ cup of seeds Rhubarb - 1 stalk	Canned fruit in fruit juice or syrup Apple, apricot, Asian pear, blackberries, custard apple, fig, jam/jelly/preserves, mango, nectarine, peach, pear, persimmon, plum, watermelon Note: allowed after Phase 2 at discretion of Practitioner

All listed quantities are per meal

PHASE 1 DIET >> REDUCE AND REPAIR			
	RESTRICTED DIET	**SEMI-RESTRICTED** Add (or increase) these foods to the Restricted Diet	**AVOID** Until further notice
GRAINS, STARCHES, BREADS, AND CEREALS	Avoid all – this includes all grains, breads, cereals, cakes, cookies	Basmati rice (cooked) - ½ cup Jasmine rice (cooked) - ½ cup Quinoa (cooked) - ½ cup	Avoid all other grains, breads, cereals, cakes, cookies except rice if approved by Practitioner
LEGUMES (LENTILS, BEANS)	Avoid	Avoid	Avoid
SOUPS	Homemade broths: beef, fish, lamb or shellfish bone broths, chicken meat broths *Limit consumption of fish bone broth*		Canned soups and soup bouillons, broths made from chicken bones
BEVERAGES	Black coffee (1 cup daily), black tea, herbal teas, water	Alcohol (clear spirits) – no more than 1 oz 2 x weekly	Beer, dark liquors and spirits, energy drinks, fruit juices, soft drinks, wine
SWEETENERS	Stevia (pure, not containing inulin)	Dextrose, glucose, organic honey (clear), stevia (pure) – no more than 2 tbs per day	Agave nectar, artificial sweeteners, maple syrup, xylitol
NUTS AND SEEDS	Almonds – 10 ea Almond flour/meal – 2 tbs Coconut: flour/shredded – ¼ cup Coconut milk – ¼ cup (without thickeners or gums) Hazelnuts – 10 ea Macadamia nuts – 20 ea Pecans – 10 ea Pine nuts – 1 tbs Pumpkin seeds – 2 tbs Sesame seeds – 1 tbs Sunflower seeds – 2 tbs Walnuts – 10 ea	Almond milk (unsweetened) – 1 cup Hazelnuts – 20 ea Pecans – 40 ea Walnuts – 3 oz	Chia, flax seeds, peanuts
CONDIMENTS	Coconut aminos (without onion or garlic), hot sauce, mayonnaise (sugarless), mustard (without garlic), wasabi Herbs and spices: fresh and dried, but not spice blends *Turmeric and ginger are particularly beneficial as they are anti-inflammatory* Vinegar: apple cider, distilled, red, white	Braggs Liquid Aminos	Asafetida, balsamic vinegar, carrageenans, chicory root, garlic, gums, onion, soy sauce, tamari, thickeners Spice sachets or pre-mixes: No maltodextrin, starches, sugar, etc.
FATS/OILS	Coconut oil, flax oil (low lignin), ghee, grape seed oil, infused oils (i.e.: chili or garlic), MCT oil, polyunsaturated vegetable oil, pumpkin seed oil, sesame oil, sunflower oil, walnut oil	Butter	Palm oil, soybean oil

All listed quantities are per meal

PHASE 2 DIET >> REMOVE AND RESTORE	REMOVE AND RESTORE	AVOID Until further notice
PROTEIN	Eggs, fish, meat, poultry	
DAIRY PRODUCTS	Butter, cheese (*aged one month or more*) E.g., Parmesan, pecorino, homemade yogurt	All other dairy products
VEGETABLES Unlimited	Alfalfa sprouts, arugula, bamboo shoots, bell pepper, bok choy, carrot, chives, cucumber, eggplant, endive, ginger, kale, lettuce, olives, parsnip, radicchio, radish, scallion, sunflower sprouts, tomatoes/sun-dried	Potato: sweet, white Starch powder: arrowroot, corn, rice, and tapioca Canned vegetables, onions, garlic, mushrooms
VEGETABLES Limited to 1 of the following per meal	Artichoke hearts – ¼ cup Asparagus – 2-3 spears Beet – 2 slices Broccoli – ½ cup Brussels sprouts – ½ cup Cabbage: green/red – ½ cup Cabbage: Napa/Savoy – ¾ cup Cauliflower – ½ cup Celery – 1 stick Celery root – ½ cup Chili pepper – 4 inches/1 oz Fennel bulb – ½ cup Green beans – 10 ea Leek – ½ ea Peas: green – ¼ cup Snow peas – 5 pods Spinach > 15 leaves/5 oz Squash/Pumpkin – ½ cup Zucchini > ¾ cup	
FRUIT Limited to 2 servings per day	Avocado - ¼ Banana - ½ Berries: all varieties - ½ cup Cantaloupe - ¼ cup Cherries - 3 Citrus - 1 piece Grapes - 10 Honeydew - ¼ cup Kiwi - 1 piece Lychee - 5 Papaya - ¼ cup Passion fruit - 1 piece Pineapple - ¼ cup Pomegranate - ½ small or ¼ cup of seeds Rhubarb - 1 stalk	Canned fruit in fruit juice or syrup Apple, apricot, Asian pear, blackberries, custard apple, fig, jam/jelly/preserves, mango, nectarine, peach, pear, persimmon, plum, watermelon Note: allowed after Phase 2 at discretion of Practitioner

All listed quantities are per meal

PHASE 2 DIET >> REMOVE AND RESTORE		
	REMOVE AND RESTORE	AVOID Until further notice
GRAINS, STARCHES, BREADS, AND CEREALS	Basmati rice (cooked) - ½ cup Jasmine rice (cooked) - ½ cup Quinoa (cooked) - ½ cup Rice cakes (plain) - 2 Rice noodles (cooked) - ½ cup	Avoid all – this includes all other grains, breads, cereals, cakes, cookies
LEGUMES (LENTILS, BEANS)	Lentils (cooked): brown – ½ cup, green and red – ¼ cup Lima beans – ¼ cup	All other legumes and beans
SOUPS	Homemade broths: beef, fish, lamb or shellfish bone broths, chicken meat broths *Limit consumption of fish bone broth*	Canned soups and soup bouillons, broths made from chicken bones
BEVERAGES	Alcohol (clear spirits) - no more than 1 oz every other day Black coffee, black tea, herbal teas, water	Beer, dark liquors and spirits, energy drinks, fruit juices, soft drinks, wine
SWEETENERS	Dextrose, glucose, organic honey (clear) - no more than 2 tbs per day Raw cocoa - 1 tsp per day	Agave nectar, artificial sweeteners, maple syrup, xylitol
NUTS AND SEEDS	Almonds - 10 ea Almond flour/meal - 2 tbs Almond milk (unsweetened) - 1 cup Coconut: flour/shredded - ¼ cup Coconut cream - 2-3 tbs Coconut milk - ¼ cup Hazelnuts - 20 ea Macadamia - 20 ea Pecans - 40 ea Pine nuts - 1 tbs Pumpkin seeds - 2 tbs Sesame seeds - 1 tbs Sunflower seeds - 2 tbs Walnuts - 3 oz	Chia, flax seeds, peanuts
CONDIMENTS	Coconut aminos (without onion or garlic), fish sauce, hot sauce, mayonnaise (sugarless), miso (fresh, not powdered), mustard (without garlic), wasabi Herbs and spices: fresh and dried, but not spice blends *Turmeric and ginger are particularly beneficial* Vinegar: apple cider, distilled, red, white	Asafetida, balsamic vinegar, carrageenans, chicory root, garlic, gums, onion, soy sauce, tamari, thickeners Spice sachets or pre-mixes: No maltodextrin, starches, sugar, etc.
FATS/OILS	Coconut oil, flax oil (low lignin), ghee, grape seed oil, infused oils (i.e.: chili or garlic), MCT oil, polyunsaturated vegetable oil, pumpkin seed oil, sesame oil, sunflower oil, walnut oil	Palm oil, soybean oil

All listed quantities are per meal

breakfasts

prosciutto, egg, and red pepper muffins

Having a few go-to meals and snacks is the key to managing your SIBO diet successfully. These muffins make a great meal while also being handy snacks to take with you. You will never get caught with nothing to eat if these are in the fridge.

- 12 free-range eggs
- 1 red pepper, diced
- 4 scallions, green part only, sliced
- 1 tbs smoked paprika
- Salt and pepper
- Ghee, coconut oil, or lard for greasing (see recipes, pages 132-133)
- 12 slices prosciutto, free from sugar and nitrates

MAKES 12

Heat the oven to 350°F.

Break the eggs into a bowl and whisk until combined.

Stir in the red pepper, scallions, and smoked paprika. Season with salt, and pepper. Mix well.

Grease a large muffin pan with ghee, coconut oil, or lard. Wrap one slice of prosciutto around the edge of each muffin cup. Spoon in the egg filling so that each muffin cup has equal amounts of filling.

Bake in the oven for 20 minutes or until cooked through.

Remove from the oven and cool slightly before serving.

These can be eaten immediately or stored in the refrigerator for a snack.

works well with:

- Italian-style pan-fried broccoli, page 85
- French-style salad, page 87
- Coleslaw, page 89

hot smoked salmon breakfast bowl

Salmon is a filling and tasty protein source. This refreshing breakfast salad can make a pleasant change, as the hot smoke cooks the fish while imparting a lovely smoked flavor to it. The quantities can easily be doubled if cooking for two.

- 2 free-range eggs (these can be omitted if you want an egg-free breakfast)
- 1 tsp coconut oil
- 1 handful mixed salad greens, washed
- 1 sprig dill, chopped
- 2 tsp olive oil
- ½ lemon, cut into half
- 1 hot smoked salmon fillet, free from sugar and nitrates

SERVES 1

In a small bowl, beat the eggs until well combined. Heat a nonstick frying pan over a medium heat. Melt the coconut oil, then pour in the eggs, turning the pan so the eggs cover the surface evenly to make a thin omelet. Cook for 1 minute, then flip and cook for another minute so both sides are golden. Remove from the heat.

Once cool enough to handle, remove the omelet from the pan and roll up like a crepe. Cut into thin strips. Set aside.

In a bowl, add the salad greens, dill, and olive oil. Squeeze ¼ of the lemon into the bowl. Take the salmon fillet and flake the meat into the bowl. Stir to combine. Serve with a wedge of lemon.

asian breakfast bowl

I love this breakfast bowl for busy days when I don't know what time I will get to eat lunch. It is very filling and keeps me satisfied for hours. What's even better is that you can make it the night before and store several portions in the fridge. All you have to do is reheat and eat.

- 1 tbs lard (see recipe, page 133)
- 14 oz free-range ground pork
- 1 tsp fresh ginger, grated
- 1 tsp fresh turmeric, grated
- 1 red pepper, diced
- 1 carrot, spiralized
- 1 zucchini, spiralized
- 4 scallions, green part only, sliced
- 2 tbs coconut aminos
- 1 tbs tomato paste
- 1 tsp apple cider vinegar
- Salt and pepper

SERVES 4

Heat a wok over a high heat. When smoking hot, add the lard and melt quickly, then add the ground pork. Stir frequently until cooked through and any liquid has absorbed.

Add in the ginger and turmeric and stir-fry for 1 minute.

Add in the vegetables, one at a time, stirring between each addition for 30 seconds. This will allow the vegetables to cook quickly, rather than crowding the wok.

Add a small amount of water if the wok gets too dry.

Stir in the coconut aminos, tomato paste, and apple cider vinegar. Season with salt and pepper as necessary. Take off the heat and serve immediately.

lemony scrambled eggs with smoked trout

The addition of lemon zest and juice lifts these scrambled eggs to something out of this world. They pair perfectly with the smoked trout and make for a very filling breakfast.

- 5 free-range eggs
- 1 tsp lemon zest
- 2 tsp lemon juice
- 1 tbs ghee or coconut oil (see recipe, page 132)
- 7 oz smoked trout, filleted
- Salt and pepper
- 2 lemon wedges

SERVES 2

Place the eggs, lemon zest, and juice in a bowl and whisk until combined.

Place a frying pan over a medium-high heat and melt the ghee or coconut oil.

Pour in the eggs and cook, stirring gently until soft scrambles form.

Season with salt and pepper to taste and serve with the smoked trout and a lemon wedge.

Zucchini fritters with crispy bacon and smoky salsa

These fritters make an excellent and filling breakfast meal. You can cook up a batch of them the night before and then just reheat and cook the bacon in the morning.

- 1 zucchini, grated
- 2 free-range eggs
- 2 tbs coconut flour
- 2 tsp ghee or coconut oil (see recipe, page 132)
- 6 strips free-range bacon, free from sugar and nitrates
- Smoky salsa (see recipe, page 130)
- Salt and pepper

SERVES 2

Squeeze the excess moisture out of the grated zucchini. You can do this by grabbing a handful of mixture and squeezing it. Liquid will escape, so do this over the sink or a bowl.

Place the zucchini in a large bowl. Add in the eggs and coconut flour. Mix to combine. If this mixture is too wet, add in a little bit more coconut flour. If the mixture is too dry, add in a drop of water. Season with salt and pepper.

Heat a large, nonstick frying pan over medium heat. Melt 1 teaspoon of ghee or coconut oil. To cook the fritters, add in a large spoonful of batter. Repeat until you have filled the pan, ensuring you have left room to flip the fritters.

Cook for 2-3 minutes on one side, then flip and cook on the other side until golden brown and cooked through. Remove from the pan and set aside.

Melt 1 teaspoon of ghee or coconut oil in the pan and add the bacon. Cook to your liking, then remove from the pan.

To serve, place the fritters on a plate with a side of bacon and a dollop of smoky salsa.

breakfast smoothies

Sometimes you don't feel like a large breakfast, so these breakfast smoothies are lovely and refreshing on a warm summer's morning.

BEAT THE BLUES

- ½ cup blueberries
- 1 cup almond milk, unsweetened
- ½ tbs coconut oil
- 1 tsp raw organic honey
- ½ tsp vanilla powder
- Ice

STRAWBERRY DELIGHT

- ½ cup strawberries
- 1 cup almond milk, unsweetened
- ½ tbs coconut oil
- 1 tsp raw organic honey
- ½ tsp vanilla powder
- Ice

BANANA MAGIC

- ½ banana
- 1 cup almond milk, unsweetened
- ½ tbs coconut oil
- 1 tsp cinnamon
- 1 tsp raw organic honey
- Ice

EACH SMOOTHIE SERVES 1

Place all ingredients for one smoothie recipe into the blender and blend until combined. Serve over extra ice cubes and enjoy immediately.

Note:

If making all three smoothies at the same time, rinse out the blender between each flavor.

vanilla and cinnamon granola

There are some mornings when you want to pay homage to your past life and eat a bowl of cereal. Although nuts can be problematic for some, for others they can be a good way of increasing good quality fats in your diet. Due to the restrictions of the SIBO protocol, this granola is to be eaten in small portions and in moderation. Divide the mixture up once you have made it so you are not tempted to overeat.

- 1 cup macadamia nuts
- ½ cup almonds
- ½ cup pecans
- ½ cup flaked coconut
- 4 tbs pepita seeds
- 4 tbs sunflower seeds
- 1 tsp vanilla powder
- 2 tsp cinnamon, ground
- 2 tbs coconut oil
- 1-2 tbs honey

CHOCOLATE VERSION:

- 4 tbs raw cocoa powder
- 4 tbs cocoa nibs

MAKES 17
SMALL PORTIONS

Preheat the oven to 350°F.

Line a large, deep baking sheet with parchment paper.

Place the nuts into a food processor and pulse until chopped to a consistency you are happy with.

Place the nuts in a large bowl. Stir in the coconut, pepita seeds, sunflower seeds, and spices.

Melt the coconut oil and honey. Pour over the dry mixture and stir until completely combined.

Pour onto the baking sheet. Cook for 10 minutes, then remove from the oven and stir thoroughly. Return to the oven. Repeat this process until the granola is golden. Remove from the oven and cool, then store in an airtight container in the fridge. Serve with unsweetened almond milk and a sprinkling of berries.

Note: keep an eye on the granola in the oven as it can burn very quickly.

To make a chocolate version, replace the cinnamon with the raw cocoa powder. Add in the cocoa nibs when you stir in the coconut, pepita seeds, and sunflower seeds.

berry good breakfast bowl

Some people prefer to eat their breakfast out of a bowl and we love how pretty these breakfast bowls can look. Use your imagination when making different smoothies and granola flavors to create a tasty combination.

- 1 serving strawberry delight smoothie recipe (see recipe, page 41)
- 1 serving vanilla and cinnamon granola (see recipe, page 43)

SERVES 1

Keep a few berries aside before making your strawberry delight smoothie. Pour the smoothie into a bowl, then top with a serving of granola. Sprinkle the remaining berries over the top and serve.

lunches

marinated lamb skewers with a greek salad

These lamb skewers are a family favorite and make for a quick yet tasty mid-week meal that everyone can enjoy.

SKEWERS

- 1½ lbs lean lamb, cubed
- 2 tbs olive oil
- 1 tbs fresh rosemary, chopped
- 1 tbs fresh parsley, chopped
- 1 long chili pepper, minced
- 1 tsp lemon zest
- 1 tsp salt
- 1 tsp pepper
- 1 red pepper, cubed
- 1 yellow pepper, cubed
- Wooden or metal skewers

GREEK SALAD

See recipe, page 91

SERVES 4

Mix all of the lamb skewer ingredients together except for the bell peppers. Allow to marinate in the fridge for 1-2 hours.

Meanwhile, if using wooden skewers, soak in warm water for 30 minutes so they don't burn on the BBQ or grill.

While the lamb is marinating, make the salad. Set aside.

Remove the lamb from the marinade and place on skewers, adding alternating pieces of red and yellow pepper to each skewer.

Heat the BBQ to medium-high.

Place the skewers on the BBQ, turning frequently until cooked through to an internal temperature of 120°F for medium-rare, 130°F for medium, and 140°F for medium-well. Remove from the heat and let rest. Serve with the salad.

salmon tartare

The use of smoked salmon imparts a lovely flavor to this tartare recipe. It works perfectly as a light lunch or appetizer and is a fun twist on the traditional beef tartare recipe.

- 4 oz smoked salmon, free from sugar and nitrates, diced
- ¼ English cucumber, thinly sliced
- 2 scallions, sliced
- ¼ avocado, sliced
- 1 tbs olive oil
- 2 tbs lemon juice
- 2 tsp fresh dill, chopped finely
- Salt and pepper

SERVES 1

Mix all of the ingredients together in a bowl, except the avocado. Season with salt and pepper.

Place the sliced avocado on a plate.

Place the tartare ingredients on top and serve immediately.

works well with:

♥ French-style salad, page 87

crustless quiche lorraine

I was in France recently and rediscovered my love for Quiche Lorraine. It is such a simple dish, yet is off-limits when treating SIBO due to the pastry, cream, and gruyère cheese. With some simple modifications, you can still enjoy this tasty meal at any time of the day or night.

- Lard for greasing (see recipe, page 133)
- 3 large strips free-range bacon, free from sugar and nitrates, chopped
- 5 free-range eggs
- 1 cup almond milk, unsweetened
- 3 scallions, sliced
- 2 oz parmesan, finely grated
- Salt and pepper

SERVES 4

Preheat the oven to 350°F.

Grease a round quiche dish with lard.

Heat a nonstick frying pan over a medium heat. Add the bacon and cook through. Set aside. Reserve a few pieces of bacon for decoration.

In a large bowl, beat the eggs until combined. Add in the almond milk and mix to combine. Add in the bacon, scallions, and parmesan. Season with salt and pepper. Stir to combine.

Carefully pour the egg mixture into the quiche dish. Top with the remaining bacon pieces. Carefully place the dish in the oven.

Bake for 40-50 minutes until the quiche is cooked through and golden on top. Remove from the oven.

The quiche can be eaten hot or cold.

works well with:

- ♥ French-style salad, page 87

zesty fish cakes with dipping sauce

If you love Asian flavors, you will love these fish cakes. Perfect as an appetizer or paired with a salad for a larger meal, they will add some zing to your day.

FISH CAKES

- 1½ lbs white fish (such as cod, haddock, etc.), skin removed, diced
- 1 long red chili pepper, minced
- 4 scallions, green part only, sliced
- 1 lemongrass stalk, white part only, chopped finely
- 1 tsp fresh ginger, grated
- 1 tbs lime juice
- ½ tsp salt
- 1 tbs coconut oil

DIPPING SAUCE

- 1 tbs sesame oil
- 1 tbs lime juice
- 2 tbs coconut aminos
- 1 tbs apple cider vinegar
- ½ tsp fresh ginger, grated
- ½ long red chili pepper, minced
- Salt

SERVES 2-4

Place the fish, chili pepper, scallions, lemongrass, ginger, lime juice, and salt in a food processor and blend until minced and fully incorporated.

Remove the mixture from the food processor and shape into small patties. Place on a tray lined with parchment, then place in the fridge until ready to cook.

In a small bowl, mix all dipping sauce ingredients together. Taste and season with salt accordingly. Set aside.

Place a nonstick skillet over a medium heat. Melt the coconut oil, then add the fish cakes. Cook for a few minutes on each side until cooked through and golden on both sides.

Serve the fish cakes with the dipping sauce.

works well with:

♥ Crunchy Asian salad, page 93

san choy bao

These tasty little parcels are surprisingly filling and fun to eat because you get to use your hands to wrap them up. Get creative and add other SIBO-friendly crunchy fillings in your lettuce wrap to personalize them just how you like.

- ½ cup macadamia nuts
- 2 tbs lard (see recipe, page 133)
- 2 tsp fresh ginger, grated
- 1 red chili pepper, finely chopped
- 2 lbs free-range ground pork
- 1 x 8 oz can bamboo shoots
- 1 x 8 oz can water chestnuts
- 5 tbs coconut aminos
- 1 tbs apple cider vinegar
- 1 tbs tomato paste, free from preservatives and sugar
- 1 tbs sesame oil
- 4 scallions, green part only, sliced
- 1 head iceberg lettuce, washed, leaves separated and kept whole
- 1 bunch Vietnamese mint, washed, leaves picked
- 2 limes, cut in half

SERVES 4

Vietnamese mint can be found in Asian markets or can be replaced with normal mint.

Preheat the oven to 350°F.

Cover a baking sheet with parchment paper and place the macadamia nuts on it. Roast for 10 minutes or until golden. Once cool enough to handle, chop roughly. Set aside.

Heat a large wok over a high heat. Once smoking, add the lard and then add the ginger and chili pepper, stirring for a few seconds before adding the ground pork. Stir quickly to break up any lumps. Brown the meat, then add the bamboo shoots and water chestnuts, stirring to combine. Add the coconut aminos, apple cider vinegar, tomato paste, and sesame oil. Stir to combine thoroughly.

If the mixture is too dry, add a few tablespoons of water.

Once cooked, remove from the heat and stir in the scallions.

Place the lettuce, mint, macadamia nuts, and lime halves on a large board. Serve the pork mixture in the wok or in a large bowl.

To make a portion, scoop some pork into a lettuce cup, top with macadamia nuts, Vietnamese mint, and a squeeze of lime. Enjoy!

aussie-style burger with the works and a side of carrot fries

Just because you are treating SIBO doesn't mean you have to miss out on burgers. You won't even notice the lack of a bun with this juicy Aussie-style burger, and the carrot fries are a fun play on traditional potato fries.

- 1 whole beet, cleaned
- 2 carrots, peeled, cut into sticks
- 2 tbs lard (see recipe, page 133)
- 10 oz ground beef
- 3 free-range eggs
- 1 tsp dried parsley
- 1 tsp dried oregano
- ½ tsp salt
- ½ tsp black pepper, freshly ground
- 4 strips free-range bacon, free from sugar and nitrates
- 4 leaves iceberg lettuce, washed
- 2 tbs mustard, free from garlic and nitrates
- Salt and pepper

SERVES 2

Preheat the oven to 400°F.

Wrap the washed, unpeeled, whole beet in foil. Place in the oven to cook for 1 hour. To check if it is cooked through, remove from the oven and pierce with a fork or small knife. If it goes into the flesh easily, it is cooked. Remove from the oven and allow to cool. The beet may release some juices while cooking and cooling, so it is best to place something underneath it to prevent staining.

Once cool enough to handle, unwrap the foil and discard. The skin from the beet will come away easily now. Peel off all of the skin and then slice thickly. Set aside.

Place the carrot sticks in a bowl. Melt 1 tablespoon of lard and pour over the carrots. Sprinkle with salt and pepper and mix to combine. Cover a baking sheet with parchment paper, spread the carrots out evenly on the sheet, and cook for 30–45 minutes or until cooked and slightly crispy.

Meanwhile, place the ground beef, 1 egg, parsley, oregano, salt, and pepper in a large bowl. Using your hands, mix until thoroughly combined and the mixture has come together. Form into 2 large patties. Place in the fridge for 30 minutes to firm.

Heat a nonstick frying pan over a medium heat. Melt 1 tablespoon of lard, then add the patties to the pan. Cook the patties to your liking. Remove from the pan.

In the same pan, add the bacon and remaining eggs and cook to your liking. Remove from the heat.

To assemble your burgers, divide the lettuce leaves across two plates. Top with a burger, 2 slices of beet, 2 strips of bacon, and 1 egg. Serve with the carrot fries and a dollop of mustard.

crispy salt and pepper calamari salad with lime aioli

Salt and pepper calamari is such a popular restaurant dish and now you can enjoy it at home while complying with your SIBO program.

- ½ cup coconut flour
- 1 tsp salt
- 1 tsp pepper
- 2 calamari, cleaned, cut into strips
- 2 large handfuls mixed salad greens
- ½ English cucumber, sliced
- 2 scallions, green part only, sliced
- 4 tbs coconut oil

SALAD DRESSING

- 1 tbs macadamia nut oil
- 1 tbs lime juice
- Salt and pepper

LIME AIOLI

- 4 tbs mayonnaise (see recipe, page 131)
- ½ tsp lime zest
- 1-2 tsp lime juice

SERVES 2

Place the coconut flour, salt, and pepper in a large bowl and mix to combine. Toss in the calamari strips and stir until coated thoroughly. Shake to remove excess flour and set aside.

In a large bowl, mix the salad greens, cucumber, and scallions. In a separate small bowl, mix together the salad dressing ingredients. Season to taste. Pour over the salad and mix thoroughly. Set aside.

In another small bowl, mix together all of the lime aioli ingredients. Set aside.

Heat a deep skillet to medium-high heat. Once hot, add in the coconut oil and melt, allowing the pan to return to temperature. To test if the oil is hot enough for shallow frying, dip a corner of one piece of calamari into the oil. If it sizzles, it is ready.

Place the calamari in the oil, being careful not to overcrowd the pan. You may need to cook it in two batches. The oil may splatter, so be careful and use a splatter guard if you have one. Cook the calamari quickly for 1 minute on each side until golden brown. Remove and drain on paper towel. Repeat until all calamari has been cooked.

Divide the salad between two plates, topping with the calamari and a drizzle of aioli. Serve immediately.

crunchy chicken tacos with coleslaw and guacamole

Be transported to Mexico with these delicious chicken tacos. They are perfectly crunchy and, combined with the creamy texture of the guacamole and zing from the smoky salsa, you'll be going back for more.

- 4 free-range chicken breast fillets, cut into 1 inch strips
- 2 tbs coconut oil, melted
- 1 tsp ground cumin
- 1 tsp ground coriander
- 1 tsp ground smoked paprika
- ½ tsp salt
- ½ tsp pepper
- 1 avocado
- 1 lime, juiced
- Salt and pepper
- Coleslaw (see recipe, page 89)
- 2 heads romaine lettuce, washed, leaves separated
- Smoky salsa (see recipe, page 130)

SERVES 4

Place the chicken strips, 1 tablespoon of melted coconut oil, cumin, coriander, smoked paprika, salt, and pepper in a plastic bag and shake to combine. Place in the refrigerator until ready to cook.

Meanwhile, make the guacamole. Add the avocado to a bowl and mash. Add the lime juice and season with salt and pepper. Stir to combine. Set aside.

Heat a grill or nonstick pan over a medium heat. Add 1 tablespoon of coconut oil. Add the chicken strips and cook until an internal temperature of 165°F is reached.

To assemble your tacos, place a spoonful of coleslaw in the base of the lettuce. Top with chicken strips, guacamole, and salsa. Enjoy immediately.

works well with:

♥ Virgin mojito, page 141

dinners

SIBO pizza with the works

When starting your SIBO treatment, many favorites may be off-limits. This SIBO-friendly pizza will become a regular fixture in your weekly meal plan. It is extremely satisfying due to the meat base and tastes just like pizza should.

- 1 lb ground beef
- 1 free-range egg
- 1 tsp dried parsley
- 1 tsp dried basil
- ½ tsp salt
- ½ tsp pepper
- ½ cup tomato purée
- 2 tbs tomato paste, free from sugar and nitrates
- ½ red pepper, diced
- ½ green pepper, diced
- ½ cup olives, in brine or olive oil (no balsamic vinegar)
- 6 slices prosciutto, free from sugar and nitrates
- 6 anchovies
- If you are in Phase 2 Remove and Restore, add 3 oz parmesan, grated (if tolerated)
- Small handful of fresh basil

SERVES 2

Preheat the oven to 445°F. Line a baking sheet with parchment paper.

Place the ground beef, egg, parsley, basil, salt, and pepper in a large bowl. Mix well with your hands until all ingredients are well combined. Roll into a large ball, then place on the prepared baking sheet. Using your hands, flatten the beef mixture across the sheet until it covers it completely and is an even thickness.

Place the sheet in the oven and cook for 10 minutes.

Meanwhile, mix the tomato purée and tomato paste together.

Remove the base from the oven. If there is some liquid on the sheet, carefully pour it off before adding the toppings.

Spread the tomato paste mixture across the base, then top with the red and green pepper, olives, prosciutto, anchovies, and parmesan (if using).

Return to the oven and cook for 10 minutes, or until cooked to your liking.

Remove from the oven, top with fresh basil leaves, and serve immediately.

works well with:

♥ Greek-style salad, page 91

best ever steak with an arugula, tomato, and prosciutto salad

Nothing beats a well-cooked steak. This dish combines the delicious BBQ flavors of the steak with the wonderful crunch of the salad. I'm sure it will be a favorite in your household, like it is in mine.

- 2 x grass-fed, free-range beef steaks
- 1 tbs olive oil
- Salt and pepper

SALAD

- 6 slices prosciutto, salt-cured, free from sugar and nitrates
- 2 tbs pine nuts, toasted
- 1 pint cherry tomatoes, halved
- 2 tbs extra-virgin olive oil
- 2 large handfuls of arugula leaves, washed
- 1 tbs red wine vinegar
- Salt and pepper
- If you are in Phase 2 Remove and Restore, add 2 oz parmesan cheese, grated (if tolerated)
- 2 tbs mustard

SERVES 2

Preheat the oven to 400°F.

Rub the steaks with olive oil, then season liberally with salt and pepper. Set aside.

Place the prosciutto on a baking sheet lined with parchment paper. Bake for 10 minutes or until crispy. Remove from the oven to cool. Once cool enough to handle, break into small pieces. Set aside.

Place the pine nuts on a baking sheet and roast in the oven for 5 minutes or until golden. Keep an eye on the nuts as they can burn quickly. Set aside.

Place the cherry tomatoes on a baking sheet and sprinkle with 1 tablespoon of olive oil, salt, and pepper. Cook for 20-30 minutes until roasted and cooked through. Remove from the oven and set aside to cool slightly.

Heat a BBQ or a grill pan until hot. Turn down the heat to medium-high. Add the steaks and cook to your liking. Once cooked, remove from the heat and cover lightly with foil. Rest for half the length of the cooking time. So if the cooking time was 6 minutes, rest for 3 minutes.

Assemble the salad while the steaks are resting. In a large bowl, mix the arugula, cherry tomatoes, prosciutto, pine nuts, 1 tablespoon of olive oil, and vinegar. Season with salt and pepper. If in Phase 2 Remove and Restore, add in the parmesan. Mix until well combined.

Serve the steak with the salad on the side. A dollop of your favorite mustard will go perfectly with the steak.

lemon and lime bbq snapper

Fish cooked on the BBQ is quintessentially summer to me. This recipe is simple yet imparts a delicious citrus flavor to the delicate snapper.

- 1 large snapper, cleaned and scaled
- 2 lemons, sliced
- 2 limes, sliced
- 1 handful fresh parsley
- ¾ inch fresh ginger, sliced
- Coconut oil for greasing
- Salt and pepper

SERVES 2

Heat the BBQ to medium heat.

Lay out some foil so that it is large enough to cover the snapper. You may need to wrap two pieces of foil around the fish if it is a large fish.

Grease the foil with some coconut oil. This will help prevent the fish from sticking to it during cooking.

Lay ⅓ of the lemon and lime slices down on the foil. Top with the fish. Insert ⅓ of the lemon and lime slices into the cavity along with the parsley and ginger. Top the fish with the remaining lemon and lime. Sprinkle with salt and pepper.

Wrap the foil around the fish, ensuring it is wrapped securely.

Place the fish on the BBQ. If you have a lid, close the lid during cooking to ensure the fish is cooked evenly. If you do not have a lid, you will need to turn the fish over halfway. Depending on the size of the fish and the heat of your BBQ, you may need to cook it for 20–40 minutes.

To check if the fish is cooked through, carefully unwrap a section of the fish and gently pull away the flesh at the deepest part. If it is opaque all the way through, the fish is cooked. Remove from the heat and serve immediately.

works well with:

- ♥ Italian-style pan-fried broccoli, page 85
- ♥ Crunchy Asian salad, page 93

succulent lamb chops with a pomegranate, pecan, and pumpkin salad

These succulent lamb chops are offset beautifully by the crunch and sweet flavor of the salad, and make a delicious and pretty mid-week meal.

- 6 lamb chops
- 1 tbs olive oil
- Salt and pepper

SALAD

- 20 pecans
- 1 cup pumpkin or squash
- 1 tbs lard (see recipe, page 133)
- 2 large handfuls mixed salad greens, washed
- 1 small pomegranate, seeds removed and retained
- 1 tbs olive oil
- 1 tbs white wine vinegar
- Salt and pepper

SERVES 2

Preheat the oven to 350°F.

Place the pecans on a baking sheet and roast in the oven for 5-10 minutes. Watch them carefully as they can burn quickly. Remove once they have roasted and slightly changed color. Set aside to cool.

Cut the pumpkin into cubes. Place in a large bowl. Melt the lard and pour over the pumpkin, then sprinkle with salt and pepper. Mix well. Place the pumpkin on a baking sheet lined with parchment paper and roast until tender and golden. This may take 30–45 minutes, depending on your oven. Remove and cool slightly.

Cover your lamb chops with oil, salt, and pepper. Heat your BBQ or grill to medium-high. Place the chops on the BBQ and cook to your liking. Remove from the heat, cover lightly with foil, and rest for half the cooking time. For example, if you cooked your chops for 5 minutes, rest them for 2 ½ minutes.

In a large bowl, mix the salad greens, pomegranate seeds, pecans, and pumpkin. In a small bowl, mix the olive oil, vinegar, salt, and pepper. Drizzle over the salad and toss well to combine.

Serve the chops with a portion of the salad.

crispy chicken strips with lime aioli

Delicious crispy chicken doesn't need to be a thing of the past while treating your SIBO. These succulent chicken strips are so easy to make and will surely be a hit in your household.

- 1 free-range egg
- 1 cup almond meal
- 1 tsp ground cumin
- 1 tsp ground coriander
- 1 tsp ground smoked paprika
- 1 tsp dried parsley
- 1 tsp salt
- 1 tsp pepper
- 4 free-range chicken breast fillets, cut into 1 inch strips
- 4 tbs coconut oil

LIME AIOLI

- 8 tbs mayonnaise (see recipe, page 131)
- 1 tsp lime zest
- 2 tbs lime juice

SERVES 4

Beat the egg in a bowl. On a separate plate, mix the almond meal, cumin, coriander, smoked paprika, dried parsley, salt, and pepper.

Dip the chicken strips in the egg. Shake to remove excess egg, then place in the almond meal mix. Cover completely, then set aside on a plate. Repeat the process until all pieces are covered.

In another small bowl, mix together all of the lime aioli ingredients. Set aside.

Heat a deep skillet over a medium heat. Once hot, melt the coconut oil, allowing the pan to return to temperature. To test if the oil is hot enough for shallow frying, use tongs to dip a corner of one piece of chicken into the oil. If it sizzles, it is ready.

Place the chicken in the oil, being careful not to overcrowd the pan. You may need to cook it in two batches. The oil may splatter, so be careful and use a splatter guard if you have one. Cook the chicken on both sides until golden brown and cooked through. Remove and repeat until all pieces have been cooked.

Serve hot with the lime aioli.

works well with:

- ♥ Coleslaw, page 89
- ♥ Crunchy Asian salad, page 93

marinated shrimp

This recipe is super easy, really tasty, and perfect for entertaining guests. The shrimp shells are full of flavor, so keeping them intact while cooking is essential. Just make sure you have plenty of bowls for the shells and napkins to clean messy hands.

- 2 lbs raw, unpeeled jumbo shrimp
- 1 long red chili pepper, minced
- ¾ inch fresh ginger, grated
- 3 scallions, green part only, thinly sliced
- 1 small bunch fresh cilantro, washed, chopped
- 2 limes
- 2 tbs coconut oil
- Salt and pepper

SERVES 4

Place the shrimp in a plastic bag and add the chili pepper, ginger, scallions, and half of the cilantro. Juice 1 lime and add to the bag. Melt 1 tablespoon of coconut oil and pour in. Add salt and pepper, then mix together. Allow to marinate in the fridge for 2 hours.

Heat a cast-iron skillet to medium-high. Melt 1 tablespoon of coconut oil until smoking. Add the shrimp and cook until pink and cooked through. Remove from the heat.

Serve with remaining cilantro sprinkled over the top and 1 lime cut into quarters.

works well with:

♥ Crunchy Asian salad, page 93

SIBO-ghetti and meatballs

Who doesn't love spaghetti and meatballs? Now you can enjoy this SIBO-friendly version with the use of zucchini noodles. If you are making this dish for children, it is a great way of adding an extra serving of vegetables to their day.

- 1 lb mix of ground beef, veal, and pork
- 1 free-range egg
- 1 tsp dried basil
- 1 tsp dried oregano
- 1 tsp dried parsley
- 4 zucchini
- 1 tbs tallow, (see recipe, page 133)
- 1 x 14 oz can whole tomatoes, no sugar or nitrates, drained
- ½ x 24 oz jar tomato purée
- 1 tbs lard, (see recipe, page 133)
- Salt and pepper
- If you are in Phase 2, Remove and Restore, you can add 5 oz parmesan cheese, grated (if tolerated)

SERVES 4

Place the ground meat, egg, basil, oregano, parsley, ½ teaspoon of salt, and 1 teaspoon of pepper in a large bowl. Mix with your hands to combine. After a few minutes, the mixture should come together nicely. Roll into small balls and place on a plate. Refrigerate until required.

Meanwhile, make the zucchini noodles. Using a spiralizer, turn the zucchini into noodles. Place in a colander and cover liberally with salt. Set aside for 30 minutes. Place in the sink as the zucchini will release liquid.

To cook the meatballs, heat the tallow in a deep, large skillet. Add the meatballs and brown on all sides. Add in the drained tomatoes and break apart with the back of a wooden spoon. Add in the tomato purée until it partially covers the meatballs. Bring to a simmer and then cook for 20 minutes or until the meatballs are cooked through.

When the meatballs are nearly done, remove the zucchini noodles from the colander. Pat dry with paper towel, removing some of the excess salt.

Heat the lard in a large, nonstick pan until smoking hot. Add the zucchini noodles, stirring quickly. Remove from the heat after 1 minute. You want them to retain their firmness and not get mushy.

Divide the noodles across four pasta bowls, top with a few meatballs, sauce, and parmesan, if using.

thai-style marinated chicken drumsticks

These Thai-style chicken drumsticks are delicious served hot or cold and make an excellent dish for a picnic.

- 2 tsp fresh ginger, grated
- 1 tsp fresh turmeric, grated
- 4 scallions, green part only, roughly chopped
- 1 long red chili pepper, roughly chopped
- 1 lemongrass stalk, white part only, roughly chopped
- 1 lime, zest and juice
- 4 tbs coconut oil, melted
- 1 tsp salt
- 8 free-range chicken drumsticks

SERVES 4

Place the ginger, turmeric, scallions, chili pepper, lemongrass, lime, coconut oil, and salt in a blender. Mix until a thick paste forms.

Place the chicken drumsticks in a plastic bag and pour the marinade over them. Place in the refrigerator for 4 hours or, preferably, overnight.

Heat the oven to 350°F. Place the drumsticks in a roasting pan and place in the oven to cook for 45 minutes or until cooked through, to an internal temperature of 165°F.

Remove and serve while warm, or they can be taken cold to a picnic.

works well with:

♥ Crunchy Asian salad, page 93

sides and appetizers

italian-style pan-fried broccoli

Broccoli is such a wonderful vegetable, but can become boring. This dish will bring the humble broccoli to life and you will be left wondering how you ever ate it plain before.

- 2-3 tbs oil from the anchovies
- 1 long red chili pepper, finely sliced
- 6 anchovies packed in olive oil
- 2 cups broccoli florets
- 2 tbs pine nuts, toasted
- Pepper
- If you are in Phase 2 Remove and Restore, add 2 oz parmesan cheese, grated (if tolerated)

SERVES 4

Heat a nonstick frying pan over a medium heat. Add the oil and chili pepper, stirring for 30 seconds. Add the anchovies and stir until they start to break down and soften. Add in the broccoli florets, stirring until mixed through with the oil, anchovies, and chili pepper.

Turn the heat to low and cover with a lid. Cook for 5-10 minutes until the broccoli is tender. If the pan gets too dry, add a few tablespoons of water.

Once the broccoli is al dente, stir in the pine nuts and season with pepper to taste. Remove from the heat.

Place into a bowl. Sprinkle with parmesan, if in Phase 2 Remove and Restore. Serve immediately.

works well with:

- ♥ Proscuitto, egg, and red pepper breakfast muffins, page 31

french-style salad

This versatile French-inspired salad is the perfect accompaniment to many meals and only takes minutes to make.

- 2 tbs extra-virgin olive oil
- 1 tbs white wine vinegar
- 1 tsp Dijon mustard, free from garlic, sugar, and preservatives
- Salt and pepper
- 1 large head of Boston lettuce, leaves separated and washed

SERVES 4

In a large bowl, mix the olive oil, vinegar, and mustard, together. Taste and season with salt and pepper.

Toss in the lettuce, coating well with the dressing.

Serve immediately.

works well with:

- ♥ Salmon tartare, page 51
- ♥ Crustless quiche Lorraine, page 53

coleslaw

Coleslaw is so easy to make and tastes delicious with homemade mayonnaise and fresh herbs. It is versatile too and can be paired with meat, fish, or poultry.

- 1 carrot, grated
- ¼ red cabbage, shredded
- 1 large handful parsley, washed, leaves picked
- 2 scallions, green part only, sliced
- 3-4 tbs mayonnaise (see recipe, page 131)
- Salt and pepper

SERVES 4

In a large bowl, mix the carrot, cabbage, parsley, and scallions together. Stir in the mayonnaise until well combined. If the mixture is too thick, you can add more mayonnaise or some lemon juice to thin it out. Season with salt and pepper.

works well with:

- ♥ Crunchy chicken tacos with coleslaw and guacamole, page 63
- ♥ Crispy chicken strips with lime aioli, page 75

greek-style salad

Who doesn't love a Greek salad? Just because you're treating SIBO doesn't mean you have to miss out on this classic salad. With a few small modifications, you won't know it's not the real thing.

- 4 large handfuls of mixed salad greens (no spinach), washed
- 4 roma tomatoes, quartered
- 1 English cucumber, sliced
- ¾ cup kalamata olives in brine or olive oil (no balsamic vinegar)

SALAD DRESSING

- 2 tbs extra-virgin olive oil
- 1 tbs white wine vinegar
- 1 tsp fresh oregano leaves
- Salt and pepper

SERVES 4

Place the salad greens, tomatoes, cucumber, and olives in a bowl. In a separate bowl, mix the salad dressing ingredients together.

Pour the dressing onto the salad and mix to incorporate thoroughly.

Serve immediately.

works well with:

- ♥ Marinated lamb skewers, page 49
- ♥ SIBO pizza with the works, page 67

crunchy asian salad

I love crunchy salads and I love Asian flavors, so this salad is a perfect combination. The fresh vegetables provide a wonderful texture while the dressing provides just enough spice without being overpowering. This pairs well with seafood, poultry, or meat, or can be eaten on its own.

- 1 cup macadamia nuts
- 1 tbs coconut oil, melted
- 1 tsp sea salt
- 2 ¼ cups shredded Napa cabbage
- 5 snow peas, sliced
- 1 large carrot, julienned
- 1 red pepper, thinly sliced
- 1 English cucumber, seeds removed, thinly sliced
- 1 large handful fresh cilantro, washed, leaves picked
- 1 large handful Vietnamese mint, washed, leaves picked

DRESSING

- 1 tsp fresh ginger, grated
- ½ long red chili pepper, finely minced
- 1 lime, zest and juice
- 1 tbs apple cider vinegar
- 1 tbs coconut aminos
- 1 tbs sesame oil

SERVES 4

Vietnamese mint can be found in Asian markets or can be replaced with normal mint.

Preheat the oven to 350°F. Line a baking sheet with parchment paper. Place the macadamia nuts in a bowl and cover with the melted coconut oil and sea salt. Stir to combine.

Place the macadamia nuts on the baking sheet and bake for 10 minutes or until golden. Remove from the oven and cool. Once cool enough to handle, chop roughly, and set aside.

Meanwhile, place the cabbage, snow peas, carrot, red pepper, cucumber, cilantro, and mint in a large bowl. Stir to combine.

In a separate bowl, mix all of the dressing ingredients together.

When ready to serve, pour the dressing over the salad and stir to combine. Top with the chopped macadamia nuts.

works well with:

- Zesty fish cakes with dipping sauce, page 55
- Lemon and lime BBQ snapper, page 71
- Marinated shrimp, page 77
- Thai-style marinated chicken drumsticks, page 81

desserts

vanilla and strawberry coconut ice

Coconut ice was a childhood favorite of mine. The good news is that you can make it SIBO-friendly. It makes a fun dessert or sweet treat without the use of sugars.

- 2 cups finely shredded coconut, free from sugar and preservatives
- 3 ½ tbs coconut butter, melted
- 3 ½ tbs coconut oil, melted
- 1 tsp vanilla powder
- 4 drops liquid stevia, no inulin
- ½ cup strawberries

SERVES 10

Place the coconut, melted coconut butter and oil, vanilla, and stevia in a bowl and mix to combine.

If the mixture is too dry, melt some more coconut oil and add it to the mixture.

Split the mixture in half.

Place the strawberries in a blender and liquefy. Pour the strawberry purée through a fine mesh sieve to remove the seeds. Stir the strawberry into one portion of the coconut mixture.

Line a loaf pan with parchment paper. Place the vanilla coconut in the base of the pan. Pat it down so it covers the entire base and is flat on the surface. Pour over the strawberry-coconut mixture and pat it down so it covers the entire surface.

Refrigerate for at least 2 hours or overnight to solidify.

To serve, remove from the pan and cut into cubes with a sharp knife.

Note: The coconut ice will get crumbly if left out of the fridge for too long, so return to the fridge when not eating. It will keep for a few days.

chocolate bark

Chocolate doesn't have to be off limits with this SIBO-friendly chocolate bark. It is most definitely worth the effort. Once you have mastered this version, play around with different flavor combinations with different nuts, seeds, and freeze-dried berries.

- ¾ cup flaked coconut, sugar-free
- ½ cup hazelnuts
- 1 cup raw cocoa butter
- ½ cup raw cocoa powder
- ¼-½ tsp powdered stevia, no inulin
- ½ tsp vanilla powder
- 2 tbs pepita seeds

SERVES 20

Preheat the oven to 350°F. Line a baking sheet with parchment paper. Place the flaked coconut and hazelnuts on the sheet. Roast for 5 minutes or until the coconut is a golden color. Remove from the oven. Chop the hazelnuts roughly. Cool.

Roughly chop the cocoa butter. Place in a plastic or silicone microwave-safe bowl. Microwave at 30 second intervals, stirring with a plastic or silicone spatula intermittently, until the mixture reaches between 105°F-113°F.

Sift in the cocoa, stevia, and vanilla powders. Stir until combined. Taste and add more stevia if required.

Cover a cool surface with parchment paper. Pour the mixture onto the parchment paper and then spread the chocolate around with a spatula until it achieves a toothpaste-thick consistency.

Scrape the thickened chocolate off the parchment paper. Return to the bowl. Heat in the microwave in 5 second intervals, stirring between each round. Heat until it is between 82°F–93°F, and all lumps have been removed.

Line a shallow baking sheet with parchment paper. Pour in the chocolate. Sprinkle with the coconut, hazelnuts, and pepita seeds. Allow to set.

Once firm, break into shards and serve.

mojito popsicles

These refreshing popsicles will cool you down on the hottest summer's day. Bursting with the zesty flavors of mint and lime, they are the perfect treat that is completely guilt-free.

- 1 lime, juice and zest
- 1 small bunch fresh mint, chopped
- 2 cups water
- 4 drops liquid stevia, no inulin

MAKES 8

Mix the lime juice, zest, mint, and water together. Add in a few drops of stevia to taste. Pour the mixture into popsicle molds, adding in wooden popsicle sticks.

Place in the freezer for several hours or overnight until frozen solid.

Enjoy on a hot summer's day.

chocolate chip mini pancakes with berry coulis and coconut cream

These mini pancakes feel like a decadent treat, yet are SIBO-friendly. The combination of the chocolate pancakes with the delicious berry coulis and the creamy coconut whip is a taste sensation that will leave you feeling very satisfied.

- 4 free-range eggs
- 2 tbs almond meal
- 2 tbs coconut flour
- 1 tbs raw cocoa powder
- 4 drops liquid stevia, no inulin
- ½ tsp vanilla powder
- ½ tsp baking powder
- 2 tbs cocoa nibs
- 1 cup strawberries
- 1 cup raspberries
- 2 tbs ghee or coconut oil
- ½ x 14 oz can coconut milk, no thickeners or gums, chilled for at least 6 hours

SERVES 4

In a large bowl, beat the eggs until well combined. Add the almond meal, coconut flour, raw cocoa powder, liquid stevia, vanilla powder, and baking powder. Mix thoroughly. Add the cocoa nibs and stir until combined. Set aside.

Set a few berries aside, then place the remaining berries in a blender and blend until liquefied. Strain to remove the seeds. Set aside.

Heat a large, nonstick frying pan over a medium heat. Melt the ghee or coconut oil. Place 4 spoonfuls of the batter in the pan. Cook for 2-3 minutes on each side. Repeat until all of the batter has been cooked.

Remove the can of coconut milk from the fridge, being careful not to shake it or move it too much. Open the can.

To serve, place 2-3 pancakes on a plate and top with a drizzle of berry coulis. Top with a spoonful of firm coconut milk from the can. Scatter with the remaining berries.

Note: Some people may not be able to tolerate baking powder as this can be made from rice flour. If uncertain, please consult with your Practitioner.

summer pineapple with coconut whip

This dessert screams 'Summer!' and is so deliciously tasty that you will keep it in your regular dessert repertoire. The pineapple is perfectly highlighted by the citrus flavors, while the coconut whip feels like a sinful treat.

- ½ x 14 oz can coconut milk, no thickeners or gums, chilled for at least 6 hours
- ½ tsp vanilla powder
- 2-3 tbs ghee or coconut oil
- 8 thin slices fresh pineapple, core removed
- 1 orange, zest and juice
- 1 lime, zest and juice

SERVES 4

Scoop out the thickened coconut cream from the top of the can, making sure not to add the watery liquid from the bottom of the can. Add in the vanilla, then whip with electric beaters until it achieves the consistency of whipped cream. Return to the fridge until ready to use.

Heat the ghee or coconut oil in a nonstick frying pan. When melted, add the pineapple, cooking on each side until golden brown.

Add in the zests and juices and bring to a boil, coating the pineapple pieces. Cook for 1 minute until the sauce has thickened.

Remove from the heat and serve immediately with a scoop of coconut whip on the side.

LF

decadent mocha mousse

You would never know this creamy decadent mocha mousse is free from dairy, egg, and refined sugar. It is so rich and filling that you only need a little to feel completely satisfied. With desserts like this, you won't feel deprived on your SIBO diet.

- 1 ripe avocado
- 2 tbs raw cocoa powder
- 1 oz strong espresso
- 3 tbs raw organic honey
- 1 cup coconut milk, no thickeners or gums, chilled for at least 6 hours

SERVES 4

Place the avocado, raw cocoa powder, espresso, and honey in a stand mixer and blend until creamy.

Change to the whipping attachment and add the firm part of the coconut milk. Don't use the watery liquid at the bottom. Whip until light and fluffy.

Spoon into bowls and refrigerate for 1 hour before serving.

raspberry soufflé

I love all French food, so it was an absolute delight when I realized I could tweak my favorite French dessert, the soufflé, to make it SIBO-friendly. Don't be afraid of the humble soufflé; it is a wonderful dessert and is sure to impress your guests. And with this summer version bursting with raspberries, you will make it again and again.

- Ghee or coconut oil for greasing
- ¼ cup honey, heated
- 1 cup raspberries
- 1 lemon, juiced
- 5 free-range egg whites

MAKES 6

Preheat the oven to 400°F.

Grease 6 ramekins with softened ghee or coconut oil.

Heat the honey until it is runny. Set aside.

Reserve 12 raspberries. Purée the remaining raspberries in a blender until liquefied. Strain to remove the seeds. Set aside in a medium-sized bowl. Juice the lemon, straining to remove any seeds or flesh. Add to the raspberry mixture.

Place the egg whites into a clean, dry bowl. Beat until soft peaks form, then slowly drizzle in the honey, beating well between each addition.

Once all of the honey has been incorporated, place a large spoonful of the meringue mixture into the raspberry mixture. Mix until well combined. You don't need to be too careful at this stage.

Next, transfer the raspberry mixture into the meringue mixture. Fold it in carefully, maintaining the light and airy texture of the egg whites.

Spoon the meringue into the prepared ramekins. Fill right to the top. Tap gently on your kitchen counter to remove any air bubbles. For a neat soufflé, scrape the top so it sits flush with the ramekin dish.

Place in a deep baking sheet. Fill halfway up the sides of the ramekins with hot water. Bake for 10-12 minutes or until the soufflés have risen and are a light golden color. Serve immediately with the remaining raspberries.

Note: Do not open the oven door during cooking as this will deflate the soufflés.

choco-coco-nutty bites

Sometimes you want a delicious treat that no one knows is SIBO-friendly. These are just the thing to curb your sweet tooth. However, it can be easy to overdo it, so keep these bites as a special treat and limit to one per serving.

- 1 tbs almond butter
- 1 tbs macadamia butter
- 1-2 tbs raw organic honey
- ¼ cup raw cocoa powder
- ¼ cup shredded coconut, sugar-free
- 1-2 tbs almond milk, unsweetened
- Extra shredded coconut, raw cocoa powder, and/or cocoa nibs for coating

MAKES 12

Mix the almond butter, macadamia butter, honey, raw cocoa powder, and coconut together in a bowl. Add in 1 tablespoon of almond milk at a time until it forms a thick paste. You don't want this paste to get too runny, otherwise it will be hard for the bites to hold their shape.

Place the extra coconut, raw cocoa powder, and/or cocoa nibs on separate plates.

Taking 2 teaspoons, scoop a small spoonful of the mixture onto one spoon. Shape it into a tight bite with the other spoon. Use the second spoon to leverage it off the first spoon and place it in either the extra coconut, cocoa powder, or cocoa nibs to coat it.

Roll it around in the coating, then set aside on a separate plate. Repeat until all of the mixture has been turned into bites and covered with a coating. Refrigerate for 1 hour to firm before eating.

snacks

chunky roast squash and macadamia dip with fresh vegetables

You will never go back to eating store-bought dips once you have had this taste sensation. Make sure you have people to share it with as you won't be able to stop at just one bite.

- 8 oz squash (raw weight)
- ¼ bunch fresh basil, leaves picked
- ½ cup macadamia nuts, toasted
- 2 tbs olive oil
- ½ lemon, zest and juice
- ½ tsp ground smoked paprika
- Salt and pepper
- Vegetable sticks to serve

SERVES 4

Heat the oven to 340°F.

Cut the squash into chunks, leaving the skin on. Roast for 30 minutes or until completely soft. Allow to cool, peel off the skin, and drain off any excess liquid.

In a food processor, blend the basil leaves to a paste, then add the macadamia nuts, olive oil, and lemon zest. This can be left slightly chunky, but blend until the larger pieces are broken down.

Add the squash pieces, lemon juice, paprika, and a small amount of salt and pepper. Pulse until combined (this won't take long), then taste and adjust seasoning if necessary.

Serve with a selection of fresh vegetable sticks for dipping: cherry tomatoes, celery, baby carrots, red/green pepper, radish, cucumber, endive and radicchio.

thanks!

With thanks to Charlotte Miller from Food & Joy for kindly allowing us to reproduce her recipe in this cookbook.

chai-spiced banana muffins

These banana muffins are a perfect mid-morning snack and are deliciously moist and aromatic. You would never know they were part of a SIBO diet.

- 4 free-range eggs
- 2 bananas, mashed
- 2 tbs raw organic honey
- 3 tbs ghee or coconut oil, melted, plus extra for greasing
- ½ cup coconut flour
- 1 tsp ground cinnamon
- ½ tsp ground nutmeg
- ½ tsp ground ginger
- ½ tsp ground cardamom
- ½ tsp ground cloves
- ½ tsp baking soda
- ½ tsp baking powder
- ¼ tsp salt
- 10 pecans
- Ghee to serve

MAKES 10 MUFFINS

Preheat your oven to 350°F.

Prepare a 12-cup muffin pan by greasing it with ghee or coconut oil, or by lining the pans with paper muffin liners. Set aside.

In a food processor, mix the eggs and bananas until well combined and free from lumps. Blend in the honey and melted ghee or coconut oil.

Add in the coconut flour, spices, baking soda, and baking powder and blend until combined.

Pour the batter into the prepared muffin pans. Place one pecan on top of each muffin.

Bake for 20–25 minutes. To test if the muffins are cooked, insert a toothpick into the center of the muffin. If it comes away clean, they are cooked.

Remove from the oven and allow to cool for a few minutes in the pan before removing and cooling on a wire rack.

These are delicious served warm with some ghee spread over them.

They can be stored in the refrigerator for a few days or kept in the freezer and reheated when necessary.

Note: Some people may not be able to tolerate baking soda and baking powder as these can be made from rice flour. If uncertain, please consult your Practitioner.

spiced trail mix

If you can tolerate nuts, this is a handy on-the-go snack. It is best to portion it out after making it so that you don't accidentally overeat your daily allowance of nuts.

- 1 cup macadamia nuts
- ½ cup pecans
- 40 almonds
- ½ cup flaked coconut, free from sugar and preservatives
- 2 tbs pepita seeds
- 2 tbs sunflower seeds
- 2 tbs coconut oil, melted
- 1 tsp ground cumin
- 1 tsp ground coriander
- 1 tsp smoked paprika
- 1 tsp sea salt

MAKES 12 PORTIONS

Preheat the oven to 350°F. Line a baking sheet with parchment paper.

Roughly chop the macadamia nuts, pecans, and almonds. Put them in a large bowl and add the remaining ingredients. Stir to combine thoroughly.

Place the mix on the baking sheet and bake in the oven for 10 minutes. Remove the sheet from the oven and stir. Return to the oven and cook for an additional 5-10 minutes, or until the mix is golden in color.

Watch the nuts carefully as they can burn quickly.

Remove from the oven. Cool completely before storing in an airtight container in the fridge.

salt and vinegar smashed sardines

Sometimes you want an easy, affordable, and filling snack. Sardines are a great option as they're portable, full of omega 3's, and will curb your hunger. Add some freshly cut vegetable sticks and it will make a perfect mid-afternoon snack.

- 1 x 4 oz can sardines, line caught, in 100% olive oil or spring water
- 1-2 tsp white vinegar
- Salt and pepper
- Vegetable sticks to serve

SERVES 1

Drain the oil from the sardines and place in a bowl. Add the vinegar and season with salt and pepper. Lightly mash with a fork to combine. Serve with vegetable sticks.

Best eaten immediately.

smoked paprika kale chips

These kale chips pack a punch. Not only are they good for you, but they satisfy those cravings for a salty, crunchy snack. Experiment with different herbs and spices to find flavor combinations you love.

- 4 large organic kale leaves
- 2 tbs coconut oil
- 1 tbs smoked paprika
- Salt and pepper

SERVES 4

Preheat the oven to 350ºF.

Thoroughly wash the kale leaves. Pat dry. Remove the tough inner stem and stalk and discard. Cut the leaves into pieces. Place in a large bowl.

Melt the coconut oil and drizzle over the leaves. Sprinkle with the smoked paprika, salt, and pepper. Stir well to coat evenly.

Line two baking sheets with parchment paper. Evenly spread the leaves over the sheets so they're not crowding each other.

Place in the oven and cook for 20-30 minutes, until crispy and dried out.

Remove and cool. Store in an airtight container. They will keep for several days.

salt and pepper pork rinds

I love crispy, salty snacks and pork rinds have become my all-time favorite snack of choice. They are a breeze to make and will have people fighting over the last piece. This is a great replacement for chips or popcorn.

- 1 free-range pork skin
- 1 tbs olive oil
- Sea salt
- Freshly cracked pepper

SERVES 4

Preheat the oven to 425°F.

Place the pork skin on a wire rack over a baking dish. This will capture the excess fat as the rind cooks.

Rub the olive oil over the skin, then sprinkle liberally with sea salt and pepper.

Place in the oven and cook for 40-50 minutes. The rind is done when small bubbles have appeared on the surface and it is a golden brown color.

Remove from the oven and cool slightly before cutting into smaller pieces.

They are delicious eaten right away as a snack or they can be used as an accompaniment to a meal.

smoked trout dip

If you have guests coming over, serve up this tasty smoked trout dip instead of commercially made dips. Not only does it taste nicer, you know exactly what has gone into it and that it is safe on your SIBO diet.

- ½ whole smoked trout, skin and bones removed
- 1 ripe avocado
- 4 tbs mayonnaise (see recipe, page 131)
- ½ lemon, zest and juice
- 4 tbs olive oil
- Salt and pepper
- Vegetable sticks to serve

SERVES 4

Place all ingredients in a food processor and blend until smooth and creamy. If your dip is too dry, add some extra olive oil. Taste and season with salt and pepper.

The dip can be eaten immediately or, if you're making it in advance, place plastic wrap over the surface of the dip to help prevent it turning brown.

Serve with vegetable sticks.

dressings, condiments and fats

smoky salsa

Salsa can be eaten as a snack or paired with a meal. Adding a dried ancho chili gives it a lovely depth of flavor and a slight hint of smokiness which is absolutely delightful.

- 1 dried ancho chili
- 6 tomatoes, seeded and diced
- 4 scallions, green part only, finely chopped
- 1 red chili pepper, diced
- 1 bunch fresh cilantro, washed and chopped
- 1 lime, juice and zest
- 2 tbs olive oil
- Salt and pepper

MAKES ENOUGH FOR ONE MEAL ACCOMPANIMENT

Rehydrate the ancho chili by placing it in a bowl and pouring boiling water over it. Soak for 10-15 minutes. Drain and then chop.

Place the ancho chili, tomatoes, scallions, chili pepper, cilantro, lime juice, zest, and olive oil in a large bowl. Stir to combine. Taste and season with salt and pepper.

Note: The ancho chili is the dried version of the poblano chili. It can be found in specialty food stores. If you can't find it, it can be kept out of the recipe.

mayonnaise

Once you have tasted homemade mayonnaise, you will never eat store-bought mayonnaise again. The key to making a successful mayonnaise is to have all of the ingredients at room temperature and to incorporate the oil very slowly. Mayonnaise can be made by hand, but a blender works perfectly for this recipe and saves your arm muscles a strenuous workout.

- 2 free-range egg yolks, room temperature
- 2 tsp Dijon mustard, free from sugar and nitrates
- 2 tsp lemon juice
- 1 cup extra-light olive oil or ½ cup extra-light olive oil and ½ cup macadamia oil
- Salt and pepper

SERVES 4

Place the egg yolks in a blender. Give them a quick pulse so they are combined. Add in the mustard and lemon juice and pulse again.

The first 1/3 cup of oil is the most important part of incorporating it into the yolks. Take your time here, otherwise the mixture might split.

Drop by drop, add in the oil, blending thoroughly between each addition. If your blender has a removable section in the lid, you can keep your motor running while you add the oil. However, pay attention to the heat generated by the motor as you don't want it cooking the eggs.

Once the first 1/3 cup of oil has been incorporated, you won't be at such a risk of separating the mixture and can start pouring it in a thin, steady stream. The mixture will thicken and start looking like mayonnaise.

Once all of the oil has been incorporated, add in 2 tablespoons of boiling water, blending quickly. This, along with the lemon juice and mustard, will help keep the mixture stable. Taste and season with salt and pepper. You may also like to add in more lemon juice or mustard at this stage.

Remove the mayonnaise from the blender and store it in a sterilized jar. Check the expiry date of your eggs, as this will be the same expiry date of your mayonnaise. Keep refrigerated.

add some zing to your mayo!

Lime aioli

- ♥ For every 4 tbs mayonnaise, add ½ tsp lime zest and 1 tsp lime juice

Lemon aioli

- ♥ For every 4 tbs mayonnaise, add ½ tsp lemon zest and 1 tsp lemon juice

3 salad dressings

You can jazz up any salad with a delicious dressing. When you make your own, you know exactly what is in it, and can alter the ingredients according to your taste.

FRENCH DRESSING

- 1 tbs olive oil
- 1 tsp Dijon mustard, free from sugar and nitrates
- 2 tsp white wine vinegar
- Salt and pepper

ITALIAN DRESSING

- 1 tbs olive oil
- 2 tsp red wine vinegar
- ½ tsp dried oregano leaves
- Salt and pepper

ASIAN DRESSING

- 1 tbs coconut aminos
- 2 tsp sesame oil
- ½ long red chili pepper, finely diced
- ½ lime, zest and juice
- Salt

SERVING: MAKES ENOUGH FOR ONE SALAD

To make the salad dressing, place the ingredients for the desired recipe in a small bowl and whisk until combined. Taste to check for seasoning, then pour over your chosen salad.

ghee

Ghee has a lovely nutty flavor and is traditionally used in Indian cooking. Ghee is simply clarified butter with the dairy proteins removed, so people with a dairy intolerance may find they can tolerate ghee. Store-bought ghee can be expensive, so why not make your own? It is easy and lasts for a long time. Make sure to buy butter made from cows that have been grass-fed.

- 3 x 8 oz butter
- 1 large glass jar, sterilized

Place the butter in a saucepan. Heat gently over a low heat. As the butter melts, a white foamy substance will rise to the surface. This is the dairy protein. Scrape this off with a large spoon. If you have someone in your house who can tolerate dairy, you can use this to make delicious pancakes for them.

As you continue cooking, the white foam should decrease until there is nothing left. The oil will also go from an opaque yellow to a clear golden color. Keep an eye on the bottom of the pan as small bits of dairy protein may fall to the bottom and burn.

Place some paper towel in a fine mesh sieve, over the sterilized glass jar. Slowly pour the hot oil over the sieve. Be careful when touching the jar as it will get very hot from the oil. Allow to cool. You can store your ghee in the fridge or at room temperature.

tastes great with:

- ♥ Fried eggs
- ♥ Pancakes
- ♥ Roasted vegetables
- ♥ Zucchini pasta
- ♥ Pan-fried fish
- ♥ Banana muffins

pork lard

You will wonder what you ever cooked with once you taste this incredible homemade pork lard. Make sure you use free-range, grass-fed pork fat so that you get the best tasting lard, not to mention supporting more humane farming practices.

- 8 oz pork fat, cut into pieces
- Water
- 1 large glass jar, sterilized

Place the pork fat pieces into a heavy-based saucepan. Pour in some water so the pork doesn't burn and stick on the bottom of the pan.

Cook gently on a medium-low heat, stirring occasionally to keep the pork from sticking to the bottom of the pan. As the pork warms, the fat will liquefy. The water will evaporate from the saucepan as the fat cooks, until there is nothing left.

Once the remaining pork pieces have turned into golden, crispy pieces and the pork fat is a light golden color, the fat is ready to be strained.

Remove the pork pieces from the fat and discard. Place paper towel over a fine mesh sieve, over the sterilized glass jar. Slowly pour the hot fat into the sieve and let it drip into the glass jar until completely strained. Cool.

Store in the fridge and use as required.

tastes great with:

- ♥ Fried eggs
- ♥ Stir-fries
- ♥ Roasted vegetables

beef tallow

Beef tallow is a wonderful saturated fat that is perfect for use as a cooking oil. It has a high smoking point and imparts a lovely flavor to your food. Make sure you use free-range, grass-fed beef fat so that you get the best tasting tallow, not to mention supporting more humane farming practices. Suet is the hard fat found around the beef loin and kidneys.

- 8 oz beef suet
- 1 large glass jar, sterilized

Place the suet in a saucepan. Cook gently on a medium-low heat, stirring occasionally to keep the suet from sticking to the bottom of the pan. As the suet warms, the fat will liquefy, leaving small pieces of beef.

Once the fat is a golden color and the beef pieces have separated, the fat is ready to be strained.

Place paper towel over a fine mesh sieve, over a sterilized glass jar. Slowly pour the hot fat into the sieve, and let it drip into the glass jar until completely strained. Cool the oil. Discard the beef pieces.

Store in the fridge and use as required.

tastes great with:

- ♥ Beef-based dishes

drinks

chilled turmeric tea

This iced tea is not only delicious, but may also provide anti-inflammatory and antimicrobial support from the ginger and turmeric.

- ¾ inch fresh turmeric, grated
- ¾ inch fresh ginger, grated
- 1 lemon, sliced
- 2-4 drops liquid stevia, no inulin
- 2 ½ cups boiling water
- Ice

If in Phase 1 Semi-Restricted, or Phase 2 Remove and Restore, you may like to add 1 tsp raw organic honey instead of stevia for sweetness.

SERVES 2

Place the turmeric, ginger, lemon, and stevia (or honey, if using) into a coffee press. Top with boiling water. Allow the tea to steep for 5-10 minutes. Press down with the plunger and strain, then chill until ready to serve.

To serve, fill two tall glasses with ice. Pour the tea over ice and enjoy immediately.

iced coffee

During the summer months, an iced coffee can be the perfect pick-me-up.

- 2 shots (2 oz) espresso
- 2 cups almond milk, unsweetened
- 2-4 drops liquid stevia, no inulin
- Ice

SERVES 2

Place all of the ingredients in a blender and blend until combined. Serve over more ice, if desired.

iced hot chocolate

Iced hot chocolate is a delicious chocolate drink on a hot summer's day, and is a great alternative to iced coffee.

- 1 tbs raw cocoa powder
- 3 tbs boiling water
- 2 cups almond milk, unsweetened
- ½ tsp vanilla powder
- 2-4 drops liquid stevia, no inulin
- Ice

SERVES 2

In a small glass, pour the boiling water over the raw cocoa powder and mix into a paste.

Place all of the ingredients in a blender and blend until combined. Serve over more ice, if desired.

virgin mojito

When you start treating your SIBO, alcohol is off-limits. This virgin mojito will be the perfect antidote, tasting just like the alcoholic version, without the headache the following day.

- 1 bunch fresh mint
- 2 limes, sliced
- 2-4 drops liquid stevia, no inulin
- 4 cups soda water
- Ice

MAKES 4 LARGE GLASSES

Place all of the ingredients in a large jug. If you like a stronger lime flavor, you can squeeze one of the limes and leave the other sliced.

Fill 4 large glasses with ice. Pour the mojito over the ice and serve immediately.

♥ Crunchy chicken tacos with coleslaw and guacamole, page 63

summer punch

On a hot summer's evening, there is nothing better than a delicious, cooling punch. This fruity concoction will keep you feeling refreshed while enjoying a very sophisticated non-alcoholic beverage.

- ½ cup berries (we used strawberries, raspberries, and blueberries)
- 1 blood orange, sliced
- 1 handful fresh mint, leaves picked
- 1 passion fruit
- 1 navel orange
- 4 cups soda water, chilled
- Ice

SERVES 4

Place the berries, blood orange, and mint in a large jug. Scrape out the pulp from the passion fruit and add this into the jug.

Juice the navel orange and add the juice to the jug.

Top with soda water and plenty of ice. Stir. Fill 4 large glasses with ice. Pour the punch over the ice and serve immediately.

Note: The flavors increase the longer you allow it to sit, so you may like to make this ahead of time and keep in the fridge until you are ready to serve. Add the ice right before serving.

VG

glossary

almond butter

Available in health food stores and becoming more widely available in supermarkets, almond butter is made from raw or roasted almonds and is a great substitute for peanut butter.

almond meal

Almond meal is made from finely ground almonds. It can be made from almonds or blanched almonds, and can be used as a flour substitute in recipes. It is available from supermarkets and health food stores.

apple cider vinegar

Apple cider vinegar is readily available in supermarkets and health food stores and can be used in many SIBO-friendly recipes. I like to use it in salad dressings and Asian cooking.

ancho chili pepper

The ancho chili pepper is the dried version of the poblano chili pepper, which originates from Mexico. It can be found in specialty food stores, and imparts a lovely, smoky flavor to dishes. It is perfect for Mexican cuisine.

bacon

Unfortunately, most commercially made bacon contains sugar and nitrates, which is to be avoided on the SIBO diet. Make friends with your local butcher and ask them to buy (or make their own) sugar and nitrate-free bacon. Organic butchers often stock it, or seek out a local artisan producer near you.

If it is impossible to find, prosciutto is a great substitute as it is often only cured with salt. Be sure to check the ingredients first though, so you don't accidentally consume something with sugar in it.

baking powder and baking soda

Both the powder and soda are often made from a base of rice flour, which is technically banned on the SIBO diet. Some people may be able to tolerate them because they are used in such small quantities. You may be able to find a suitable variation from your local health food store, but always check the ingredients and, if in doubt, speak to your Practitioner before consuming.

butter

Dairy can be problematic for many people so if you think it might cause you problems, reintroduce it slowly. I look for butter made from grass-fed cows that contains minimal ingredients. Not only do I disagree with intensive farming or feeding cows grains, but I also think butter tastes significantly better when the cows have been able to roam freely, eating grass. Your local health food store will be able to tell you which butter is made from 100% grass-fed cows. I use this butter to make my own ghee.

cocoa nibs

Available from health food stores, cocoa nibs are roasted and chopped cocoa beans. They have a chocolately taste, but don't contain sugar so aren't sweet. They can be used to add extra crunch and flavor as well as being a great decoration for desserts.

coconut aminos

This is a great alternative to soy sauce. It is available from health food stores or online. Check the ingredients list as some brands use garlic and onion flavorings, which are not SIBO-friendly.

coconut butter

This is made from the meat of a coconut which has been ground down to a very smooth and fine consistency. I find coconut butter lovely and sweet and would often eat a teaspoon of it when first overcoming my sugar cravings. It is available in health food stores and select supermarkets.

coconut flour

Made from the dried flesh of the coconut, which is then milled into a fine powder, coconut flour makes an excellent substitute to gluten-based flours. It does have a coconut flavor to it, so I prefer to use it in dishes that are sweet or Asian in flavor. In addition, it is more absorbent than traditional flours, so you don't need to use as much.

coconut cream and milk

Coconut cream and milk are made from the flesh of a coconut. It is grated and then soaked in hot water. The cream rises to the surface, which is then scooped off. The remaining milk is strained through a cheesecloth. Look for a brand that doesn't use thickeners or binders and is 100% coconut.

coconut oil

Coconut oil is now available in mainstream supermarkets, which makes it much easier to buy. It has a high smoke point, which makes it safe to use when cooking at high temperatures. It has a long shelf life and doesn't need refrigeration. I like to use it in Asian dishes and desserts as I find it can impart a coconut flavor to the food.

free-range eggs and poultry

I simply do not agree with intensive farming practices and do not purchase chicken, meat, or eggs that are not free-range. There is much debate around the validity of the free-range regulations, so I research farmers that are transparent about their production. You are more likely to have truly free-range eggs from your local health food store or farmers market than you are from a supermarket.

fish and seafood

Our oceans have been over-fished so, where possible, it is best to buy sustainably-caught fish and seafood. I always buy local seafood. Not only has it traveled fewer miles, but it isn't exposed to the chemicals and antibiotics used with some imported fish and seafood.

grass-fed meat

I always choose grass-fed meat. I support animals being able to roam and eat the food they were designed to eat and am concerned about consuming meat from animals who themselves have consumed grains. Speak to your butcher about where they source their meat from and what practices they use to raise their cattle.

macadamia butter

Similar to almond butter, macadamia butter is made from ground macadamia nuts and can also be used as a substitute to peanut butter.

organic produce

Getting your head around eating for a SIBO diet can be hard enough, so don't worry if you can't buy organic produce. If you are concerned about ingesting chemicals on your fruit and vegetables, you may prefer to buy organic options from *The Dirty Dozen:* foods that are more likely to absorb more chemicals and pesticides than others.

1. Apples
2. Celery
3. Grapes
4. Peaches
5. Blueberries
6. Potatoes
7. Spinach
8. Nectarines
9. Bell Peppers
10. Strawberries
11. Lettuce
12. Cucumber

raw cocoa butter

Raw cocoa butter is the extracted fat from the raw cocoa bean and is pale yellow in color. It is the base for chocolate and has a lovely chocolatey aroma. However, it is not at all sweet and needs to be mixed with other ingredients to make it palatable. It is available in health food stores and select supermarkets.

raw cocoa powder

Raw cocoa powder is made from raw cocoa beans and contains antioxidants and enzymes. Traditional cocoa powder is made from roasted cocoa beans, which, unfortunately, reduces its beneficial properties. It is available in health food stores and select supermarkets.

raw organic honey

If you can tolerate it, honey has incredible healing properties. However, most commercially-made honey has been heated, which diminishes these properties. Look out for locally-made raw, organic honey made from bees who are busily working in your local area. Honey is high in fructose, so avoid it if you have fructose malabsorption.

smoked salmon

Some commercially-prepared smoked salmon can be cured with sugar, so be sure to check the ingredients before purchasing to be certain it doesn't contain sugar. Choose wild salmon over farmed salmon where possible.

stevia

Stevia is a shrub whose leaves can be used as a substitute for sugar. It is 200 times sweeter than sugar so it should be used sparingly. It also has a distinct flavor that may not be suitable in some dishes. It is available in many forms, but only the ground leaves and 100% natural liquid stevia (without inulin) should be used on the SIBO diet. To tell if your powdered stevia is 100% natural, all you need to do is check the color. If it is green, it is natural. A white powder means it has been processed. Both are available from health food stores.

turmeric

Turmeric is available fresh from Asian grocery stores or in powdered form, which is available widely from supermarkets. It imparts a strong yellow color to food and the raw roots can easily stain nails, skin, and clothing once cut. Don't wear your favorite white clothing when cooking with fresh turmeric in case it accidentally stains. I love the flavor it adds to dishes and it can be used with a variety of foods.

unsweetened almond milk

Most commercially-made almond milks contain some form of sweetener such as honey, rice syrup, corn syrup, or cane sugar. These sweeteners can be problematic with your SIBO and should be avoided. Look out for unsweetened almond milk, but be careful to check the ingredients to ensure it doesn't contain inulin or other thickeners, gums or binders, which can irritate the gut. To be safe, it is best to make your own almond milk, because then you know exactly what is in it.

vanilla powder

Vanilla powder is ground vanilla beans. It imparts a wonderful vanilla flavor to dishes, but does not contain other ingredients like vanilla extract does. This makes it safe to eat while on a SIBO diet. It is available from health food and specialty stores.

resources

This is a list of some of my favorite resources that have helped me through my journey of understanding my body and how I could heal it. It is by no means an exhaustive list, but these are the ones I've really enjoyed. I hope you find value from them too.

books

I particularly love David Perlmutter MD's books on the brain and the gut respectively. A neurologist, he is recognized internationally as a leader in the field of nutritional influences in neurological disorders and presents fascinating and insightful information in the following books.

- ♥ Perlmutter, D 2014, Grain Brain: The Surprising Truth about Wheat, Carbs and Sugar, Hodder & Stoughton, Great Britain.
- ♥ Perlmutter, D 2015, Brain Maker; The Power of Gut Microbes to Heal and Protect Your Brain – For Life, Hodder & Stoughton, Great Britain.

Giulia Enders delivers an exceptionally engaging, informative, and interesting tour of our gut. Delving into how it works, what's in it, and its importance in our everyday life, it is a must-read for anyone interested in understanding the inner workings of one of our least understood organs.

- ♥ Enders, G 2014, Gut, the inside story of our body's most under-rated organ, Scribe Publications, Brunswick, Australia.

Dr. Mark Pimental is one of the pioneers in SIBO research and has written about his research into it, believing it to be one of the major underlying causes of IBS.

♥ Pimental M 2006, A New IBS Solution. Bacteria: The Missing Link In Treating Irritable Bowel Syndrome, Health Point Press, Sherman Oakes, CA

This is the book that first introduced me to the concept that food could harm as much as it could heal the human body, and that every person is different in the way we respond to food.

♥ D'Adamo, Dr P J D 1998, Eat Right For Your Type, Century Books Limited, London, UK.

Although quite heavy at times, this book by Nora T. Gedgaudas is an interesting read if you are interested in how the human body developed from our pre-agricultural Paleolithic ancestors.

♥ Gedgaudas, N 2009, Primal Body, Primal Mind. Beyond The Paleo Diet for Total Health and a Longer Life, Healing Arts Press, Rochester, Vermont.

This book is a must-read if you have ever wondered how you put on weight. Gary Taubes explains the body's processes in an easy-to-understand manner, answering many life long questions of how and why.

♥ Taubes, G 2010, Why We Get Fat: And What to Do About It, Anchor Books, New York, USA

This is another excellent book from Gary Taubes, this time exploring the theory around carbohydrates instead of fats being to blame for the obesity and diabetes epidemics.

♥ Taubes, G 2007, Good Calories, Bad Calories: Fats. Carbs. And The Controversial Science of Diet and Health, Random House, New York, USA.

Australian author David Gillespie is a recovering corporate lawyer. After gaining 90 pounds, he set out to discover why he was fat. Reviewing how the body converts and stores fat, this is a fascinating read into the perils of sugar consumption.

♥ Gillespie, D 2008, Sweet Poison: Why Sugar Makes Us Fat, Penguin Group, Melbourne, Australia

Another book by David Gillespie explores why diets don't work, how to lose weight permanently, and who are the real culprits of ill health and weight gain.

♥ Gillespie, D 2015, Eat Real Food. The Only Solution to Permanent Weight Loss and Disease Prevention, Pan Macmillan, Sydney, Australia.

Melissa and Dallas Hartwig are the creators of the Whole30 program, which teaches people how to eat real, whole food while removing processed junk. This book is an easy read and explains why common foods such as sugar, grains, and dairy aren't great for our health.

♥ Hartwig, M; Hartwig D 2012, It Starts With Food: Discover the Whole30 and Change Your Life, Victory Belt Publishing Inc

cookbooks

I am a big fan of Australian author Irena Macri. Her cookbook, *Eat Drink Paleo*, has been a staple in my house and is well-used, as all of her recipes are delicious and easy to make.

♥ Macri, I 2015, Eat Drink Paleo Cookbook, Penguin Group, Australia.

Claire's cookbook was one of the first I found when beginning the journey of healing my gut. A fellow Australian, she is a Nutritional Medicine Practitioner and co-founder of *Rejuvenated for Life*.

♥ Yates, C 2013, Optimum Health the Paleo Way, Exisle Publishing Pty Ltd, Wollombi, Australia.

Simple, easy, tasty, and straight-forward recipes are delivered by Melissa Joulwan from *The Clothes That Make The Girl*. These recipe books have been staples in my kitchen.

♥ Joulwan, M 2013, Well Fed; Paleo Recipes for People Who Love to Eat, 8th edition, Smudge Publishing, Austin Texas.

♥ Joulwan, M 2013, Well Fed 2; Paleo Recipes for People Who Love to Eat, 8th edition, Smudge Publishing, Austin Texas.

websites and digital resources

Dr. Nirala Jacobi ND is considered Australia's leading natural health expert on SIBO. Dr. Jacobi has worked in the natural health industry in the United States and Australia for 20 years, and has been in clinical practice for over 18 years. She currently offers breath testing in Australia for SIBO diagnosis. Her website is full of information regarding SIBO and contains a preliminary quiz that may indicate if a person may be suffering from SIBO.

♥ Sibo Test
sibotest.com sibotest

Dr. Allison Siebecker is known in SIBO circles as the *Queen of SIBO.* Her website houses a host of information, articles, and YouTube videos that are a wonderful resource and should be an important part of your SIBO education.

♥ Dr. Allison Siebecker, ND MSOM LAc
siboinfo.com

Popular blogger and author of the *Eat Drink Paleo Cookbook*, Irena Macri's website is jam-packed with great recipes.

♥ Eat Drink Paleo
eatdrinkpaleo.com.au

Michelle Tam is another popular paleo blogger who houses a site full of delicious recipes, while adding some fun and quirkiness with her cartoon characters.

♥ Nom Nom Paleo
nomnompaleo.com

Robb Wolf has a great site for paleo nutrition and lifestyle.

♥ Robb Wolf
robbwolf.com

Mark's Daily Apple is a handy resource for all things primal, with recipes, exercise and lifestyle tips.

♥ Mark's Daily Apple
marksdailyapple.com

The *Whole9* and *Whole30* websites are handy resources when you're getting your head around changing your lifestyle and eating habits. Some tough love is dished out, which was particularly useful for me.

♥ Whole 9 & Whole 30
whole30.com

Chris Kresser is a practitioner of integrative medicine and a licensed acupuncturist, offering health and wellness programs and nutrition-focused articles.

♥ Chris Kresser
chriskresser.com

movies and documentaries

Australian Damon Gameau embarked on a journey to discover the effects of sugar on the body by only eating a healthy low-fat diet.

- That Sugar Film
  thatsugarfilm.com

This Oscar-nominated documentary looks at the food industry's harmful effects on the planet and human health.

- Food, Inc
  takepart.com/foodinc

This was the first documentary I watched that showed how damaging fast food could be to the human body in a very short amount of time.

- Super Size Me

This documentary explores the underlying causes of childhood obesity in America. Katie Couric narrates the documentary. It was nominated for the Grand Jury Prize at the Sundance Film Festival.

- Fed Up
  fedupmovie.com

references

I would like to thank Dr. Nirala Jacobi ND for allowing me to reference information on the SIBO Bi-Phasic Diet Protocol in this book. Further information can be found on SIBO, the SIBO Bi-Phasic Diet Protocol, and testing in Australia at sibotest.com.

FOR MORE HANDY RESOURCES
to support your SIBO journey, head to thehealthygut.co/resources

live well with SIBO

The Healthy Gut podcast

SIBO Cooking Show

SIBO recipes

SIBO Coaching Program

SIBO events

SIBO shopping tours

thehealthygut.co/sibosummer

info@thehealthygut.co

index

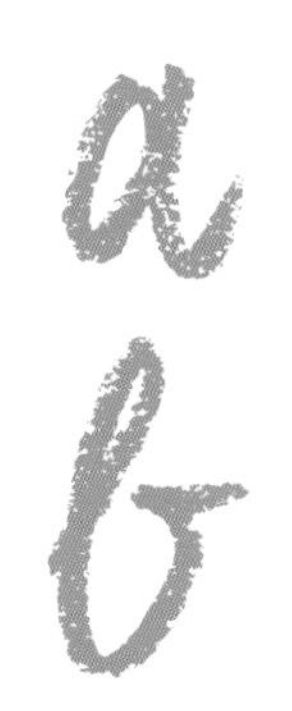

Acknowledgements 6

bacon

Crustless quiche Lorraine 53
Zucchini fritters with crispy bacon and smoky salsa 39

banana

Chai-spiced banana muffins 117

beef

Aussie-style burger with the works and a side of carrot fries 59
Best ever steak with an arugula, tomato, and prosciutto salad 69
SIBO-ghetti and meatballs 79
SIBO pizza with the works 67

berries

Berry good breakfast bowl 45
Chocolate chip mini pancakes with berry coulis and coconut cream 103
Raspberry soufflé 109
Vanilla and strawberry coconut ice 97

breakfasts

Asian breakfast bowl 35
Berry good breakfast bowl 45
Breakfast smoothies 41
Chocolate granola 43
Hot smoked salmon breakfast bowl 33
Lemony scrambled eggs with smoked trout 37
Prosciutto, egg, and red pepper muffins 31
Vanilla and cinnamon granola 43
Zucchini fritters with crispy bacon and smoky salsa 39

broccoli

Italian-style pan-fried broccoli 85

C

chicken

Crispy chicken strips with lime aioli 75
Crunchy chicken tacos with coleslaw and guacamole 63
Thai-style marinated chicken drumsticks 81

chocolate

Chocolate chip mini pancakes with berry coulis and coconut cream 103
Choco-coco-nutty bites 111
Chocolate bark 99
Chocolate granola 43
Decadent mocha mousse 107
Iced hot chocolate 139

coconut

Chocolate chip mini pancakes with berry coulis and coconut cream 103
Choco-coco-nutty bites 111
Summer pineapple with coconut whip 105
Vanilla and strawberry coconut ice 97

desserts

Choco-coco-nutty bites ... 111
Chocolate bark ... 99
Chocolate chip mini pancakes with berry coulis and coconut cream ... 103
Decadent mocha mousse ... 107
Mojito popsicles ... 101
Raspberry soufflé ... 109
Summer pineapple with coconut whip ... 105
Vanilla and strawberry coconut ice ... 97

dinners

Best ever steak with an arugula, tomato, and prosciutto salad ... 69
Crispy chicken strips with lime aioli ... 75
Lemon and lime BBQ snapper ... 71
Marinated shrimp ... 77
SIBO-ghetti and meatballs ... 79
SIBO pizza with the works ... 67
Succulent lamb chops with a pomegranate, pecan, and pumpkin salad ... 73
Thai-style marinated chicken drumsticks ... 81

dips

Chunky roast squash and macadamia dip with fresh vegetables ... 115
Smoked trout dip ... 127

dressings

Asian dressing ... 132
French dressing ... 132
Italian dressing ... 132

drinks

Chilled turmeric tea ... 137
Iced hot chocolate ... 139
Iced coffee ... 139
Summer punch ... 143
Virgin mojito ... 141

eggs

Crustless quiche Lorraine ... 53
Lemony scrambled eggs with smoked trout ... 37

fats

Ghee ... 132
Lard ... 133
Tallow ... 133

Foreword ... 8

fish

Hot smoked salmon breakfast bowl ... 33
Lemon and lime BBQ snapper ... 71
Lemony scrambled eggs with smoked trout ... 37
Salmon tartare ... 51
Salt and vinegar smashed sardines ... 121
Zesty fish cakes with dipping sauce ... 55

Glossary ... 144

kale

Smoked paprika kale chips ... 123

lamb

Marinated lamb skewers with a Greek salad ... 49
Succulent lamb chops with a pomegranate, pecan, and pumpkin salad ... 73

Live well with SIBO ... 152

lunches

Aussie-style burger with the works and a side of carrot fries ... 59
Crispy salt and pepper calamari salad with lime aioli ... 61
Crunchy chicken tacos with coleslaw and guacamole ... 63
Crustless quiche Lorraine ... 53
Marinated lamb skewers with a Greek salad ... 49

Salmon tartare ... 51

San choy bao ... 57

Zesty fish cakes with dipping sauce ... 55

m

Mayonnaise ... 131

muffins

Chai-spiced banana muffins ... 117

Prosciutto, egg, and red pepper muffins ... 31

My story ... 10

n

nuts

Choco-coco-nutty bites ... 111

Chocolate granola ... 43

Chunky roast squash and macadamia dip with fresh vegetables ... 115

Spiced trail mix ... 119

Vanilla and cinnamon granola ... 43

p

pineapple

Summer pineapple with coconut whip ... 105

pizza

SIBO pizza with the works ... 67

pork

Asian breakfast bowl ... 35

San choy bao ... 57

Salt and pepper pork rinds ... 125

SIBO-ghetti and meatballs ... 79

prosciutto

Prosciutto, egg, and red pepper muffins ... 31

r

raspberry

Chocolate chip mini pancakes with berry coulis and coconut cream ... 103

Raspberry soufflé ... 109

Resources ... 147

s

salads

Crispy salt and pepper calamari salad with lime aioli ... 61

Crunchy Asian salad ... 93

Coleslaw ... 89

French-style salad ... 87

Greek-style salad ... 91

seafood

Crispy salt and pepper calamari salad with lime aioli ... 61

Marinated shrimp ... 77

sibo

The SIBO Bi-Phasic Diet Protocol ... 20

SIBO treatment options ... 16

What is SIBO ... 12

Smoky salsa ... 130

snacks

Chai-spiced banana muffins ... 117

Chunky roast squash and macadamia dip with fresh vegetables ... 115

Salt and pepper pork rinds ... 125

Salt and vinegar smashed sardines ... 121

Smoked paprika kale chips ... 123

Smoked trout dip ... 127

Spiced trail mix ... 119

squash

Chunky roast squash and macadamia dip with fresh vegetables ... 115

t

turmeric

Chilled turmeric tea ... 137

w

Welcome ... 7

z

zucchini

SIBO-ghetti and meatballs ... 79

Zucchini fritters with crispy bacon and smoky salsa ... 39

Thank you so much for creating and sharing this wonderful book with healthy, hearty, and delicious meals for people with SIBO. I am just glad to know that there is a cookbook that I can utilize to help me with my healing path as we both know that diet is an integral part of it.

Thank you for contributing this wonderful resource to the SIBO community.

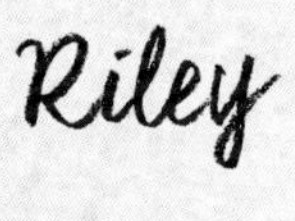

Oh my goodness. That lamb with pomegranate, pecan, and pumpkin salad was TOTALLY amazing!!! The whole family loves the recipes. I love the granola..... it has been over 12 months since I have had any "cereal" type food and it has been sooooo gooood......

I'm so thrilled to find something to make life a bit easier. No need to tell you how easy it is to start to flounder with this condition.